1998
Guide to Good Food
in the
Westcountry

> *Hotels*
> *Restaurants*
> *Pubs*
> *Cafés*
> *Guesthouses*
> *Farmhouse Bed & Breakfasts*

edited by
Tom Jaine

HALSGROVE

First published in Great Britain in 1997 by Halsgrove

British Library Cataloguing-in-Publication Data
CIP data for this book is available
from the British Library

ISBN 1 874448 27 2

The publication of this work was enabled by
grant aid given under Objective 5b EAGGF
Funds.

Published by Halsgrove in association with
The Taste of the West

HALSGROVE
Publishing, Media and Distribution
Halsgrove House
Lower Moor Way
Tiverton
Devon EX16 6SS

Tel: 01884 243242
Fax: 01884 243325

Illustrations by Moish Sokal

Printed in Great Britain by BPC Information Ltd, Exeter.

Contents

Westcountry Cooking
is about the three Ws.
What,
Where,
and
When.

What: ingredients and materials should be as far as possible local; and they should be fresh.

Where: cookery should reflect the locality, the place, its history and development; the effect of geography and climate on materials available; and the traditions and preferences of the community.

When: cooks should work with the seasons, not against them.

Introduction

Westcountry Cooking

The Westcountry Cooking initiative is concerned with food and its provision to the general public, whether visitors to the region or residents. Participants are headed by the National Union of Farmers and Taste of the West, the co-operative of speciality food producers, and the West Country Tourist Board. Individuals who have played their part include local restaurateurs and hoteliers, food writers, farmers and producers, chefs, cooks and journalists.

The idea is not to disinter a long-dead historical cooking tradition. It is to recognize that the concept of a regional cuisine is entirely valid, and that a region's characteristic produce will be a direct reflection of its geography, geology and climate, as well as its social history and present predicament. Regional dishes, whether old or new, will evolve naturally.

It is a two-pronged fork to identify and encourage local produce and to act as catalyst to chefs and cooks. Instead of resorting to the nearest supermarket, frozen-food supplier, or pan-national dealer, cooks should turn in the first instance to growers, farmers and shops on their doorstep. Rather than blind imitation of international recipes, this initiative hopes to encourage the development of dishes that best reflect the locality, materials that are at hand, and the season in which they are cooked. These dishes may be new, or may revitalize the old, traditional cookery.

This guide is a first selection of establishments in the region that have expressed support of Westcountry Cooking's aims and objects. The venture is still young, and as other places will see the wisdom of it, so more will be included. They range from country-house hotel to café, tea shop, or farmhouse bed and breakfast. It includes only those places that serve lunch or dinner, so guest houses that cook breakfast but not an evening meal, are not to be found here.

Entry depends on support of our general aims, proof that a significant proportion of fresh, local produce is used, and that each establishment has available for customers a list of its principal suppliers of fresh ingredients.

Is there such a thing as regional cooking?

Westcountry Cooking is anxious to avoid the pitfall of rushing helter-skelter into a twee world of revivalism and false nostalgia for the past glories of English cookery. We all know that too often it was absolutely dreadful. Who wants to revisit lumpy custard, or greens boiled to rags?

Westcountry Cooking is more interested in the present, though not dismissive of the past, and particularly keen to encourage a sense of place or locality. Hence its emphasis on regional cooking.

Many chefs, cooks and diners are envious of the larger countries of Europe who celebrate regionalism through recipes, styles and ingredients. They point to the success of French provincial cookery as a form, and a means of generating culinary enthusiasm. They relish the immense differences between northern and southern Italy, or between Galicia, the Basque country and Andalusia in Spain. They have also witnessed the updating of these local distinctions encapsulated by the French phrase *cuisine de terroir* which avoids the mere pursuit of grandmother's local recipes, substituting instead a recognition that locality or place is the essential wellspring of a chef's imagination and provides the principal ingredients.

Identifying regionalism in Britain is more difficult. The country can be reduced to its original nationalities: English, Welsh, Scots, and Irish. That affords a broad and valid framework. But is further subdivision possible? So much of daily life has been blanketed by a mantle of uniformity as communications break down barriers between one district and the next. Education and economic activity have similar effects; and the sheer mobility of the population, up and down the social classes, and from one area to another have eroded local difference. These influences have been felt for centuries. It is as if the last true phase of regionalism was the Anglo-Saxon settlement after Rome's retreat, when seven kings ruled, not one.

England is also a small country, though densely occupied. Our teachers were constantly banging on about how no other place had more varied landscape in so small a compass, but this pales to insignificance against the scale of France, Germany or Spain, or the length and breadth of Italy. Regionalism, in a country the size of England, comes close to parochialism.

Whatever the truth of these comments, it is also true that many modern disciplines – statistics, demographics, sociology, and market analysis – recognize important differences between areas, or districts, or regions in England. Tastes are not the same, and they vary from place to place as well as from income bracket to income bracket. Beer, tobacco, housing, furnishings, motor vehicles, sweets and confectionery: all are subject to regional preference; why not, therefore, food and cookery?

A century ago, it was axiomatic that if two families sat down to a meal on the same day but in two distinct regions, their food would be different. Variation would extend to methods of cookery, fats and cooking mediums, staple ingredients, the structure of the meal itself, and preferred dishes. As one went up the social scale, these differences would probably reduce, as lifestyles melded into a common standard disseminated by court, capital city and university. Equally, going down the scale to the underclass, poverty and destitution would inhibit the exercise of choice. But it would be true for the middling sort – which compares, a little at any rate, with the regionalism of French bourgeois cooking.

In the intervening years, these differences have been eroded. Other influences on diet have been brought to bear: travel, education, literacy and the diffusion of information through the press, film and broadcasting. But if we are to avoid the paradox of reducing choice through extending the range of our culture – which causes the decline of pockets of variation in pursuit of new, but common horizons – we need to rediscover a sense of place, or locality.

Regionalism in food and cookery may be likened to modern vegetable gardening. Our quest for regulation and harmonization has caused the demise of innumerable local varieties of fruit and vegetables. Their withdrawal from general usage has set alarm bells ringing at the possible effect on the gene pool and our future capacity to maintain the health and viability of any particular species. Similarly, if we let our appreciation of place go hang, and if we consign all old recipes linked to locality and former social organization to the waste-bin, then we sacrifice an important source of change and inspiration. We will have instead to rely on foreign cooks, foreign ingredients, and foreign flavours. We already do enough of that, let's not do it entirely.

How do we define regional cookery?

The six counties of Gloucestershire, Somerset, Wiltshire, Dorset, Devon and Cornwall constitute the South Western Region defined by the Registrar General and other government agencies. It takes in several geological types, and contains variations in history and human geography that encourage some parts to look to other groupings of counties or population centres, but there are the foundations of a common style of food and cookery that are capable of development.

A litany of particular dishes is one way to define a regional cuisine, but it needs more than that to achieve coherence. The accidents of individual recipes need to draw on shared ingredients and approaches to cooking. To make an analogy with architecture: that houses are built from the same materials, or conform to the same principles of structure, is more important than the incidentals of surface design, for example the shape of window panes. For a culinary parallel, think of south-western France. Geese and ducks give the region its special identity. Their by-products (fat, innards, and *foie gras*) provide a structure for a self-contained style of cookery; the birds themselves are important ingredients; and shared methods of cooking (the *confit* for example) unite one community with another.

The Westcountry has a common medium, and significant mainstay ingredients that inform and reach out to the furthest corners of everyday cooking. The dairy farming and pasturage of the South West give beef on the one hand but more importantly milk, butter, cheese, cream and clotted cream to provide a medium (butter), a vital added ingredient (clotted cream), a staple of everyday diet (cheese) and by-products that support further regional specialization (whey for yoghourt production, or for pig farmers). Thus agriculture and cookery are locked into a single cycle.

Another specialization has extended its influence into the whole spectrum of cookery: orchards and cider production. Although beer has its place (I think especially of the white ales of South Devon recorded from early modern times), cider has provided a distinctively regional drink, its own commercial infrastructure for public sale (the infamous cider houses), and a flavouring for cookery – as well as another pillar of the diet of pigs who can gorge on windfalls in the orchards or be fed the pomace or pulp from the cider press. Eating and cooking-apples have influenced diet and recipes in their turn.

Fish should count as much as the dairy industry towards defining a regional cuisine: from the latter-day speciality of smoked mackerel, to the species that are found, or have been caught in earlier years. Brill, pilchards, elvers, lampreys, mullet, hake, mackerel and sprats might be thought regional; we land more crab than any other area of Great Britain; scallops, mussels and oysters are longstanding favourites; and there are several important salmon rivers.

The three groups of ingredients I have listed permeate more than just a few dishes. They contribute to a lifestyle, to daily reality. That other parts of the country have also adopted them does not disguise their regional origin – which should be celebrated.

Perhaps less widespread in their influence, but none the less excellent and worth celebrating, are individual ingredients found or grown in the region from a comparatively early stage in our development. Among many I could cite saffron, cabbages in Paignton, broccoli and cauliflower on the south coast, Wiltshire crayfish, rock samphire and laver, seakale (first domesticated in south Devon), port wine that developed out of the Newfoundland fishery trade, salt cod from the same, and the products of the pig found throughout north Wiltshire.

If you take these several items as a whole, it could be strenuously maintained that only the South West can produce this particular combination – a reasonable test of regional identity.

The mask does not slip when it comes to specific recipes and ways of cooking. There does seem an identifiable preference for cooking pies, from the pasty – a pie with an historical function – to the squab pie in several variations (pork or mutton and apples), apple pies in Dorset and

Devon, or the lamprey pie sent annually to the monarch by the Corporation of Gloucester. There are also recipes that are specific to the area: Chudleighs or Cornish splits, saffron bread, Bath buns, Sally Lunns, Bath chaps, the stargazey pie and many, many more.

Westcountry Cooking and regional cookery

I said at the outset that Westcountry Cooking wants to avoid the blind alley of false nostalgia, is not merely concerned with reviving recipes that may not longer appeal to our tastes or whose function is now redundant. Many Westcountry dishes were born out of poverty and deprivation or the need to substitute workaday ingredients for impossible luxuries. These conditions may no longer apply.

Another difficulty, were history to be the only arbiter of 'Westcountry', is that so many dishes have travelled beyond the region or are common to more than one English district. Boundaries are fuzzy. Boundaries are also false. People have been happy to call junket a Devonshire dish, but junket was made the length and breadth of England. Sometimes a recipe is tied to a region by erroneous antiquarianism. A cookery writer finds a manuscript note of a recipe in the library of a particular country house or rectory. That recipe is immediately given regional status. But it is quite possible the original copyist simply transmitted instructions gained from elsewhere in the country. The number of copper-bottomed, guaranteed regional recipes is smaller than sometimes claimed.

This is why Westcountry Cooking is principally concerned with the fusion of locality and materials, not nit-picking about whether recipe A belongs, or whether recipe B is more correctly from Berkshire or Huntingdon. What makes cookery regional today, and will allow a regional style to develop, is recognition that *where* you cook matters, and that local, fresh materials will inform *how* you cook.

This guide is therefore a celebration of kitchens that embrace their locality. Sometimes they will be cooking things in a way quite foreign to the South West, but if they use ingredients grown or reared nearby, and they use them at the proper time of year, they are in fact extending the range of regional cookery, but not destroying its meaning.

Support from within the profession

Here are two statements by a cook and an hotelier, working in Devon and Somerset respectively, that define what regional cooking has meant to them. The first is by Kit Chapman of the Castle Hotel in Taunton, where he has guided a succession of chefs towards reliance on their local producers, and to a better understanding of what is meant by English cookery.

'If you enjoy good food; if the rhythms of the garden and countryside bring you pleasure and if you live where we live, then to buy strawberries from Spain, lamb from New Zealand or cheeses from France seems absurd.

'Produce, climate and geography define our cooking. We lie at the heart of the Westcountry – a lush peninsula providing a rich larder. So we seek out keen gardeners to grow fruits, vegetables and herbs for us. Equally, Somerset is a dairy county – it produces over twenty varieties of cheese (ewe and goat, as well as cow) – so it would be daft not to offer some of them to our guests.

'Local marketing – a strong rapport with our suppliers and growers – a deep sense of place and a natural sympathy with the traditions of this region are the benchmarks of our kitchen. This is what distinguishes the Castle from a restaurant in London or Rome, Bangkok or Sydney. And that's what makes eating here more interesting.'

The second statement of support comes from Tina Bricknell-Webb of Percy's Restaurant at Virginstow in Devon:

'Like the man who liked the product and then bought the company, Percy's wanted fresh produce and so bought a farm on the Cornwall/Devon border to grow it. The experience of fresh flavours on a plate led to Percy's being Good Food Guide Local Produce Champion of 1997.

'Having heard of Percy's accolade, many producers nearby knocked on our door to offer their wares: freshly picked logan-berries, woodcock, snipe, pheasant and grouse, giant puff ball and chanterelle mushrooms, goat's and ewe's milk cheeses, clotted cream and the like. We are always searching for unusual ingredients and would like to encourage more.

'The South West is a haven for passionate artisans producing anything from hand-made cheeses to rare-breed meats. Day

*boats issue forth from Cornish ports returning with some of the
best fish available in the country. With this wealth of prime
produce on our doorstep, why shop anywhere else?'*

A Guide to Westcountry Cooking and the Westcountry Cooking Initiative

This *Guide* is one element of the initiative. *The Westcountry
Cooking Suppliers Guide* will also be published, compiled by
Taste of the West. It will list as many producers, wholesalers
and retailers of fresh foods in the region as possible. It is
designed to help those catering establishments that wish to
buy local and buy fresh to do so, which is not always as
straightforward as it ought to be. The cookery writer
Michael Raffael is editing a series of books, *Westcountry
Cooking,* which will offer regional recipes old and new,
historical curiosities and recipes tied to place. Each volume
will deal with an ingredient or group of ingredients. The
first two are focused on *Cream* and *Baking* respectively.
Others will follow, on cider, pickles and preserves, wild
food, vegetables and so on.

Entry into this *Guide* has been decided by the editor and
is based on the consensus view of his collaborators as to an
establishment's worth and standards. It has also depended
on establishments subscribing to the objects of Westcountry
Cooking, but not to the payment of any fee or inducement.
In subsequent editions, it will be possible to take into
account the views of you, the reader. There is a form at the
end of this book which you can send to the offices of the
Guide to help us extend its reach and to ensure standards
are maintained.

Different kitchens, and different forms of catering, mean
that many styles of cookery are present in this book. The
historically-minded reader will note that traditions are best
kept up by the country people who open their houses as
farmhouse bed & breakfast or holiday accommodation.
Pubs, too, have often more ability to present food that was
never intended to grace an elaborate or fancy table. Cafés
can show off cakes and pastry to greater advantage than
hotels. But hotels and restaurants are great places to find
fish and shellfish.

Some of the establishments listed in this book give information about the sources of their ingredients in each menu distributed to visitors. Westcountry Cooking applauds this openness. It shows a kitchen supporting its mainstay; it gives customers a chance to visit suppliers to make their own purchases for consumption at home. Westcountry Cooking is adamant that establishments should use local suppliers of fresh produce in the production of their food, and that details about the origin of raw materials should be available to all-comers.

How to use this guide

CONSTANTINE 1

H 2

Trengilly Wartha Inn 3

Nancenoy, Constantine, TR11 5RP. 4

🍴 **12.00–14.15 (bar only), 18.30–21.30 (bar meals), 19.30–21.30 (restaurant).** 5

Annual closure: no food on Christmas Day. 6

☎ **01326 340332.** 7

🚪 **1 mile outside Constantine, sign-posted off the Gweek road.** 8

🍴🍴 **£26.** 9

🛏 **£40.** 10

🛏 **£56.** 11

☀ **12**

Westcountry dishes: Falmouth Bay scallops. 13

1 Establishments are listed by county and in alphabetical order of town or village. See the map for details of location.

2 H: hotel; R: restaurant; R (with rooms): restaurant with rooms; P: pub; C: café; B&B: bed and breakfast; Farmhouse B&B: bed and breakfast on a working farm that is part of an accredited farm accommodation scheme. These categories may sometimes be arbitrary. Some pubs prefer to view themselves as inns or primarily as restaurants; some restaurants like to be thought hotels. The description here is a shorthand convenience, and does not represent a judgement one way or another.

3 Name of the establishment.

4 Address.

5 🍴 Opening hours. In general, the hours given are times when full meals are served. Pubs and hotels, for example, have longer hours when other food in bar or brasserie may be available. Days of the week when establishments are open are also recorded, unless they are open every day.

6 Annual closure: a note is given here of any fixed holidays or closed periods during the year. The information has been provided by the establishments themselves.

7 m Telephone number. If there is a separate fax line, this is also noted.

8 w Directions for motorists. These are only given where there is difficulty finding the establishment, particularly when it is far from any other settlement.

9 zz The price of a full meal. This is a general guide only, and makes no allowance for extravagance or acute hunger. It is the basic price of three courses, half a bottle of house wine, and a cup of coffee. In very many instances, food and drink may be bought for less.
Bar meals in pubs and light lunches in hotels are two examples. Cafés provide a much greater range as well. Where a marked difference between lunch and dinner prices has been noticed, it is recorded.

10 a The price of a single bedroom (or a double room used as a single) and breakfast. This is a guide price only, and records the starting point of any establishment's tariff. Many hotels may vary their charges according to which room is occupied, or the time of year the visit is made.

11 s The price of a double bedroom and breakfast. The reservations made for 10 apply.

12 M Denotes in the Cornwall section which establishments are members of the 'Food in Cornwall' Association.

13 Westcountry Dishes. This note draws attention to dishes cooked at an establishment in the past year that be fairly described as 'Westcountry'. By definition, everything cooked might qualify, so I have taken the liberty of selecting some that are more or less traditional or noteworthy. Readers should not expect these dishes to appear on every menu at any time of the year. Entries in this section are somewhat arbitrary.

Cornwall

Introduction

'Consider, for example, what a chicken has to suffer anywhere in London. As soon as plucked it has its poor breast broken to make it look plump: it is then packed for market in sawdust, the turpentine of which races through its delicate flesh; lastly it is baked in a gas-heated oven wherein the fumes of coal-tar fight it out with the infection already absorbed. That is your townsman's notion of a "roast chicken." It bears no resemblance at all to a Cornish chicken marketed in a clean napkin, seasoned with lemon-thyme and other herbs from the garden, roasted on a spit and thoroughly basted in the process, especially when accompanied by home-made bread that has taken the delicate aroma of a furze-heated oven.'

So wrote the Cornish poet Arthur Quiller-Couch in his introduction to the county Women's Institute cookery book of 1930. Details change (not least the furze-heated oven), but the principle remains.

There are plenty of reasons for treating the cookery of Devon and Cornwall together, for there are many obvious connections. Yet each county does have an identity and particularity all its own. There are variations, for example, in the way clotted cream is made and used. Differences are reinforced by the old saying that the Devil never crossed the Tamar into Cornwall on account of the Cornish propensity for putting everything into a pasty. This handy portable meal for fishermen, miners, or farm workers – all eating away from home – was always linked specifically to the county, even though it could be found as readily in Devon and Somerset. (I speak of time before the national distribution of the form.) 'We went to a pastry cook's and bought some Cornish "pasties" for lunch, a sort of turnover with meat and potatoes inside, instead of fruit or preserve,' wrote the diarist Francis Kilvert, on a visit from the Wye valley in the middle of the last century, in search of a convenient picnic.

Historically, Cornish food was marked by the presence of the sea and the poverty of much of its people. It was not a cuisine de luxe. Although there are few large towns, tin mining meant there was a large group of industrial workers, as well as fishing communities on the coastline, and the farming villages of the eastern part. The county was strong Chapel, making it more like Wales (another Celtic borderland) than the soft London visitor might expect. The Cornish are also good at rugby football, brass bands and choral singing.

Wet weather and barren heaths meant Cornwall once depended more on barley and oats of the marginal highland zone than lush wheat of the lowlands and this is reflected in traditional cookery, even if the warmth of a Cornish spring meant that gardens and the nooks and crannies of the southern coast were fantastically productive and free from frost and blight.

Tourism has produced its rash of restaurants, hotels, cafés, pubs with a strong emphasis on food and many farmhouses offering excellent accommodation. The fearsome landlady with high tea at six o'clock sharp is more a product of the northern seaside than of Cornwall, where the buxom, floury-handed farmer's wife has perhaps held centre-stage. It is farms that preserve the most memory of things as they used to be, while restaurants and hotels make their contribution by cooking fish (with the bonus of a pudding or two).

Small-scale producers are not as thick on the ground in Cornwall as in other south-western counties, but it is still possible to get farmhouse clotted cream and butter, decent sausages, a few cheeses, and much fruit and vegetables grown earlier, and often better, than elsewhere. Fish from Porthleven or Newlyn, or oysters and mussels from Port Navas, are, of course, supreme.

Some local dishes:

Cornish pasty	*Potato cakes*
Stargazey pie	*Saffron cakes*
Fish pie	*Cornish splits*
Crab soup	*Black cake*
Chicken and parsley pie	*Heavy cake*
Herby pie	*Barley bread*
Leek or likky pie	*Apple dappy*
Mutton and turnip pie	

CALSTOCK
H
Danescombe Valley

Lower Kelly, Calstock, PL18 9RY.

 19.30.

☎ **01822 832414; fax 01822 832446.**

⊟ **half mile W of Calstock village along lane parallel to river.**

⊗⊗ **£40.**

⇱ **£125.**

The situation of this early nineteenth-century house with a two-storey verandah is enviable: a view of the Tamar sweeping round Cothele, with the railway viaduct in the middle distance. Martin Smith has studied the art of getting big-city visitors to unwind. He should write a book: 'Zen and the art of rustic relaxation', perhaps. In his wine list of great intelligence (Italians are extra-special) which includes vintages from Sharpham Vineyard on another Devon river, the Dart, and a daily-changing menu of four courses – which include a board of anything up to a couple of score of unpasteurized Devon and Westcountry cheeses – he has two arrows in his sheaf of weapons to unwind with. He comments that they do not cook pasties or stargazey pie, but that, 'all our dishes are by definition Westcountry, by cooking them here and using local produce.' This is a good point. Certainly, the restrained (often Anglo-Italian) style of the cooking lets the materials sing out, throwing into relief the quality of the vegetables gathered from fields a step away from the kitchen door, or the salmon from the Tamar itself.

CHAPEL AMBLE

P

Maltsters' Arms

Chapel Amble, PL27 6EU.

🍴 **12.00–14.00, 18.00–21.30.**

Annual closure: Christmas Day evening.

☎ **01208 812473.**

🍴🍴 **£16.**

David and Marie Gray have kept this pub as well-loved as any village inn in the county. Friendly atmosphere, provision of no-smoking room, good food, dry white wine by the glass from Camel Valley Vineyards: all reasons put forward for success. (When did pubs serve anything by the glass except the very worst in boxes? How fortunate that begins to change.) Bar and restaurant menus have lots of fish. In winter months when trade is less frantic, lucky customers will have home-made pasties to keep them going through the day. Steak and ale pie may not be particularly Cornish, but the beef certainly is, and the beer too. Marie Gray also reports they do 'raw fry potatoes', sounding very like potato 'jowdle', a Cornish supper dish of potatoes and onion covered with water and fried until soft.

Westcountry dishes: fillet of pork with cider and cream; Cornish pasties; steak and ale pie.

CONSTANTINE

H

Trengilly Wartha Inn

Nancenoy, Constantine, TR11 5RP.

🍴 **12.00–14.15 (bar only), 18.30–21.30 (bar meals), 19.30–21.30 (restaurant).**

Annual closure: no food on Christmas Day.

☎ **01326 340332.**

🚪 **1 mile outside Constantine, sign-posted off the Gweek road.**

£26.
 £40.
 £56.

This inn overlooking Polpenwith creek on the Helford river has become ever more popular. By day, you eat in the bar; in the evening, in bar or restaurant. A steady printed menu is supplemented by a board with daily specials. Fish is the main attraction: Port Navas oysters, scallops from Falmouth Bay cooked oriental-style with ginger and spring onions, a nice fry-up of crisp mixed fish, crab cakes, or something like a chunk of cod with creamed leeks and fennel. Home-made steak and kidney pudding features on Wednesday, and every day there is some weighty pudding like sticky toffee or cranberry to give ballast to the homeward journey. Westcountry cheeses, of course, and wine from Pemboa Vineyard, their closest producer, as well as English fruit wines from Porthallow.

Westcountry dishes: Falmouth Bay scallops.

CRACKINGTON HAVEN
B&B
Manor Farm
Crackington Haven, EX23 0JW.
19.00 (residents only).
Annual closure: Christmas Day.
☎ 01840 230304.
from £45 (incl. dinner).
from £80 (incl. dinner).

Manicured lawns and sculpted hedges surrounding this large farmhouse are impressive monuments to a gardener's labour, just as Muriel Knight's dinners are signal of much work in the kitchen. She impressively combines the traditional with the modern. A meal last year began with savoury bread and butter pudding, went on to cod with pink peppercorns and a lime vinaigrette served with Cornish new potatoes and little moulds of seakale, then finished with a pear crumble tart and clotted cream. Her haddock pasties are micro not macro: small enough to start a meal. They serve as reminder that the Cornish pasty was not necessarily filled with meat and potato: it could have any filling under the sun. Its distinction was not the filling but the presentation which made the filling portable. That savoury bread and butter pudding can also be found at the Tea Shoppe in Dunster, Somerset.

Westcountry dishes: Devon apple cake; haddock pasties with clotted cream.

CRACKINGTON HAVEN
FARMHOUSE B&B
Trevigue

Crackington Haven, EX23 0LQ.
🍴19.30.
Annual closure: Nov–Feb.
☎ **01840 230418.**
🚌 **take the B3263 to Boscastle from the A39 Bude–Camelford road, the farm is down the lane signed to High Cliff (National Trust).**
🍴🍴 £19.50.
🛏 £30.
🍽 £40.

Five hundred acres, two and a half miles of coastline, licensed for marriages, a sixteenth-century courtyard house with mullioned windows, and a cliff 731 feet high on the doorstep (to sober you up). The farm has its own Wessex Saddlebacks for pork and sausages, and Devon cows for beef. Janet Crocker's cooking is more than farmhouse fare. Menus have a wide range and choice, but still explore the possibilities of what comes to hand, not just the cold cabinets of the local supermarket: soup of wild mushrooms gathered in their woods and fields, venison with blackberry sauce, or smoked trout with a sorrel mayonnaise. The traditional also gets an outing, be it a trifle, heavy with Cornish cream, or under roast (beef, potatoes and onion simmered and baked together), or pork cooked with dumplings or simmered in cider with apples and apricots.

Westcountry dishes: pork in cider with apple rings and herb dumplings; Cornish under roast.

CRACKINGTON HAVEN
FARMHOUSE B&B

Treworgie Barton

Crackington Haven, EX23 0NL.

🍴19.00.

Annual closure: Oct, Dec–Jan (advance booking only, Nov, Feb, Mar).

☎ **01840 230233.**

🚇 **turn to Crackington Haven at Wainhouse Corner on A30 S of Bude, then turn for Millook.**

🍴🍴 **£14 (unlicensed).**

🛏 **£36.**

A low wall keeps sheep from straying into the front garden of this long, low building set on the sensational coastline south of Bude. The house is centuries old, and one can imagine the long cold nights endured by hill farmers in the dead of winter without electricity or mod. cons. Not today; all is sweet comfort, and there is Pam Mount cooking for the next meal: a cream tea, glazed collar of ham with spiced apricots, or chicken with a watercress sauce. Farmhouse cooking with a lift to it, from flavours lent by all the green-stuffs coming from the garden, the home-baked bread, and clotted cream made by hand.

Westcountry dishes: pork chops with apples, cream and cider.

CURY
FARMHOUSE B&B
Tregaddra Farm

Cury, TR12 7BB.

🕎residents only.

☎ 01326 240235.

🚍 from Helston take A3083 to the Lizard for 5 miles.
Turn left at Wheel Inn; half mile, first farm on left.

🕎🕎 £13.

🛏 £18.50.

🍽 £39.00.

Figgy pudding was recorded in a Victorian dialect dict-
ionary as being 'much in vogue among men in Devon and
Cornwall'. Things have not changed. It was then, and still is
at June Luggy's farm, a raisin suet pudding. Figs meant
raisins, but they might also mean figs: 'figgie hobbin' was a
Cornish recipe for a suet paste mixed with chopped dried
figs and baked in the oven. ('Hobbin' was dialect for oven.)
In a tiny village on the way to the Lizard, with the science
fiction landscape of Goonhilly Down in the background,
can be found this working farm – which supplies its own
beef for the table – with well appointed bedrooms, heated
swimming pool for colder days, and an immaculate garden.
June Luggy keeps a farmhouse table: substantial roasts with
trimmings, good fresh vegetables, traditional British
puddings. Another Cornish variation she is proud of is the
cobbler that she serves instead of Yorkshire pudding. A
cobbler is often thought of as a fruit pie from America, but
it may also refer to any sort of pie with a very thick dough.
Latterly, this has become a scone mixture served with meat.

Westcountry dishes: figgy pudding; Cornish cobblers.

GILLAN

H

Tregildry

Gillan, TR12 6HG.

🍴 19.00–20.45.

Annual closure: Nov–Feb.

☎ 01326 231378.; fax 01326 231561.

🍴🍴 £25.

🛏 from £55 per person incl. dinner.

Panoramic views across the Helford river keep people's eyes wandering during otherwise gripping conversation at this stylish hotel run by Huw and Lynne Phillips. Huw Phillips' cooking is as full of zip as the look of the place and a nightly menu offers plenty of contrast within a short compass. There is not a lot of traditional Cornish in the repertoire, but much that is fresh and of the locality. Megrim sole are topped with vegetables, prawns and capers and finished with a lemon butter, sea bass comes on caramelized red cabbage, salmon with saffron couscous. Cheeses are only Westcountry.

Westcountry dishes: saffron and crab tartlet; pork cutlet served with caramelized apple and cider sauce.

GOLANT

H

Cormorant Hotel

Golant, PL23 1LL.

🍴 19.00–21.00.

☎ 01726 833426.

🚗 2 m N of Fowey, reached from the B3269: down the hill to the water's edge.

🍴🍴 £21.

🛏 £35.

🛏 £70.

St Sampson is the patron of Golant church, and the name of the wine produced in the village – found on the Cormorant's wine list. A glass or two of that may put a different perspective on the sensational views over the estuary from the terrace. Golant does wine, it also does fish: perhaps the clearest signpost to location on the menu in the relaxed dining-room, where a menu offers some fairly lively flavours (curry and banana with chicken, chilli with prawns, teriyaki sauce with surf'n'turf) as well as a pick of that day's potting and netting: red mullet, scallops, prawns, mussels, crab, salmon and sole for example. It's a good place too for Cornish lamb.

Westcountry dishes: brochette of scallops.

GUNWALLOE
P
Halzephron Inn
Gunwalloe, TR12 7QB.
🍴12.00–14.00, 19.00–21.30 (21.00 Sun).
Annual closure: Christmas Day.
☎ 01326 240406.
🍴🍴 £21.60.
🛏 £35.
🛏 £56.

For half a century the Halzephron (the name derives from the Cornish for 'the cliffs of Hell') was without a licence, a private house. Before, it had been a haunt of smugglers and wreckers (the hellish cliffs doubtless yielding their dividend): a tunnel shaft is the evidence. Today, it is the creation of the Davy Thomases, and they have put it firmly on the traveller's map. Concentrate on the daily blackboard for excellent fresh fish, and applaud their naming of the individuals who supply their crab (Mark Kearsley), beef (John Retallack), and many other ingredients. 'Helston pudding' takes us back to the days when vast numbers of steamed puddings and cakes were named after towns, individuals or events. Often the connection might have been a coincidence, at the very least tenuous. Helston Pudding is a steamed suet pudding with dried and candied fruit and a little spice.

Westcountry dishes: crawfish stew; Helston pudding.

HELSTON
H

Nansloe Manor

Meneage Road, Helston, TR13 0SB.

🍴 12.00-13.30, 19.00-20.30.

☎ 01326 574691; fax 01326 564680.

🚗 **Turn right at roundabout by Helston Community Hospital, hotel 3rd on the left.**

🍴🍴 £32.

🛏 £41.

🛏 £78.

The Manor is in a secluded valley on the edge of town. Views are peaceful and just the spot for those keen on aeronautics: Culdrose RNAS is not far away for thrilling choppers and more. The house is a listed building, decoration sparkling, and the food is in the mode of modern British cookery. With fish from Newlyn and meat from Retallack, the fine butcher at St Keverne, materials are never less than topnotch. They are incorporated into creations such as breast of chicken with string-vegetable spaghetti , or plaice on cabbage scented with cinnamon and served with smoked bacon, or steak with lentils and a mushroom and chestnut sauce. The Riddens stock three wines from the Pemboa Vineyard nearby.

KINGSAND
P

Halfway House Inn

Fore Street, Kingsand, PL10 1NA.

🍴 12.00–14.00, 19.00–21.30.

Annual closure: Christmas Day.

☎ 01752 822279; fax 01752 823146.

🍴🍴 £21.50.

🛏 £22.

🛏 £44.

Ten yards from the waterfront, the expectation of well-cooked fish is excited and satisfied in this popular inn on the west bank of the Tamar. There's a lively appreciation of more recipes than fillets in batter, be it scallops cooked with lentils and white wine, or puffs of crab in an Italian pesto sauce, and there is an enviable range of fish served, witness the eel stew. One Westcountry recipe for this dish involves cider, carrots and mushrooms.

Eel is none too common nowadays, except perhaps as part of a smoked fish platter (then it often comes from Holland). Sarah Riggs, who shares kitchen duties with Alan Ogilvie, mentions using seaweed to give that briny ammoniac tang to sea bass, and samphire (the rock samphire of the Southwest, not the marsh samphire of East Anglia) to perform much the same task.

Samphire has always been a distinguished partner, for instance of salmon, in Devon and Cornwall fish cookery. Although specialists in fish, the list of meats is also impressive. Often there is ox tongue, for instance cooked with cannelini beans, and much game and poultry like venison, quail and guinea fowl.

Westcountry dishes: Cornish eel stew; sea bass with seaweed.

LANHYDROCK
R
Lanhydrock House
Lanhydrock, PL30 5AD.
12.00–15.00 (Mar–Oct).
Annual closure: Jan–Feb, limited opening Nov–Dec.
☎ 01208 74331; fax 01208 74084.
£16.25.

The Westcountry properties of the National Trust have been undergoing culinary reconstruction. Sara Paston-Williams, their adviser, herself no mean historian of England's food heritage, has been urging them to look further into traditional recipes, and to rely on local suppliers and producers for their materials. Results have been enlivening. As most visitors come to the house by day, tea in the Servants' Hall or the Housemaids' or Housekeeper's Rooms is as important a meal as lunch. Try the genuine Cornish splits (a similar dough to baps), which are served with cream – when they came with cream and treacle, they were known as 'thunder and lightning'. At lunchtime, there is a chance to eat squab pie. This may have been called after young pigeons, but was made in Cornwall with any meat that came to hand, from cormorants (young) and duck to mutton and pork. The constant was layering the meat with apple and onion. One rather elaborate old recipe called for cormorant, veal, ham, mutton, beef and a top layer of pilchards. All this was moistened with clotted cream: all of Cornwall in a pie crust. The Cornish under roast is a way of baking meat under a layer of potato. At Lanhydrock they serve Wild Beef from Richard Vines in Chagford, and Manx sheep (a rare breed of tasty hill sheep) which come from an NT farm at Bosigran in west Cornwall.

Westcountry dishes: squab pie; Cornish under roast; Cornish splits.

LAUNCESTON
FARMHOUSE B&B
Hurdon Farm
Launceston, PL15 9LS.
🍴18.30, evening meal not available Sun.
Annual closure: Nov–Apr.
☎ 01566 772955.
🚗 take the A388 towards Launceston from the A30 bypass, then the road signed to Trebullet.
🛏 £15.50.
🍽 £31.

Lovers of kitchen antiques will gaze at the granite fireplace with trivets, pothooks, Dutch oven and many other survivals. Proof, if proof is needed, of the pedigree of this house, at the centre of a large farm that is still working in dairy, beef, lamb, pig and potato production. The kitchen, now with more up-to-date equipment, is supplied with some fine ingredients and Margaret Smith and Nicola Stanbury turn them into store items, such as jams and preserves, as well as day-to-day dishes, to keep family and guests replete. Mrs Smith mentions mashed potato with saffron, recalling that Cornwall continued to use that precious commodity, for instance in breads and cakes, long after the rest of the country. It was a favourite in the Middle Ages for its flavour, but more especially because they loved golden, extravagant, food. Apple dappy, another local dish she mentions, is a scone mixture, rolled up with chopped apple, soaked and then baked in a lemon syrup.

Westcountry dishes: creamed potato with saffron; apple dappy.

LISKEARD
R
Bacchus Bistro
18 Pike Street, Liskeard, PL14 3JE.
🍴12.00–14.30, 19.00–22.30 Mon–Sat except Sat lunch;
Sun jazz lunch from 13.00.
☎ 01579 347031.
🍴🍴 £20.

There are many cooks in the region who look beyond their locality for inspiration yet depend upon it for fresh and genuine supplies. Thus you get the best of modern provincial cooking. Michael Green is one such. Happy to mix a robust Italian bean stew with curly Cornish kale, or construct new-wave pasties with courgettes and basil, or even filled with fruit and served with a mascarpone ice-cream. It is not the aim of this guide, or the whole Westcountry Cooking initiative, to support only those who open their history books to create a 'heritage cookery'. The octopus cooked here with lemon grass and dill is indeed local (the Cornish squid fishery went from strength to strength in the early 1980s), yet if you turn to a Victorian book that details edible fishes in the South West (*Fish, How to Choose and How to Dress*, written by William Hughes ['Piscator'] of

Falmouth in 1843), you will find no mention of either octopus or squid. Bacchus is full of laughter, or jazz – and much good food with an Italian or Mediterranean tilt. Ingredients are often heightened with strong herbs or garlic, and imaginative combinations result: celeriac mash with hot roast chestnuts and walnut oil; calf's liver with balsamic vinegar, crème fraîche and braised kale; home-smoked field mushrooms with a cheese stuffing, are three examples. The coincidence was too strong for Michael Green not to stock Camel Valley Vineyards' Bacchus wine.

Westcountry dishes: Octopus with lemon grass and dill.

LOSTWITHIEL
P
Royal Oak
Duke Street, Lostwithiel, PL22 0AQ.
12.00–14.00, 18.30–21.30.
Annual closure: Christmas Day.
☎ 01203 872552.
£12.50.
£33.50.
£55.

The pub has medieval origins, but is Mecca for beer fanatics for the very wide range on pump or in bottle. Eileen Hine is in charge of the kitchen – won a national prize for her stuffed mushrooms – and maintains a constant printed menu that is on a par with many other pubs for range and style, but also does some fine home-cooking whether of daily changing fish dishes, or more interesting stews or braises or pies. Her 'cow pie' is a beef and ale pie, much liked.

Westcountry dishes: pork in cider; wild boar; 'cow pie'.

LOSTWITHIEL

<u>R</u>

Trewithen Restaurant

3 Fore Street, Lostwithiel, PL22 0BP.

19.00–21.30 (summer: Mon–Sat; winter: Tues–Sat).
Annual closure: 2 weeks in springtime.

☎ **01208 872373.**

£27.

Brian Rolls has been tending the stoves at the Trewithen for many years and has come to know well suppliers and customers alike. It is a good place to eat lobster, offered in a number of ways, and he also offers a menu of Cornish food. An example began with soused mackerel, then on to a cheese soup made with Yarg, garnished with 'mini oggies'. (Tiddy Oggie is recorded as a Somerset recipe with a filling of pork, bacon and cheese.) The main course is the Trewithen version of stargazey pie, using scallops and monkfish and a 'stargazing' prawn, before a dessert of apple pancakes. Here is an instance of local traditions being reworked to create something new.

MAWGAN

<u>R</u>

Yard Bistro

Trelowarren, Mawgan, TR12 6AF.

12.00–14.00 (Tues–Sun), 19.00–21.00 (Wed–Sat).

☎ 01326 221595.

((((£10.00 (lunch), £18.00 dinner).

The house, and bistro, are at the end of a long driveway. The courtyard setting puts people at their ease, and on a fine summer's day a cream tea is just the ticket. Trevor Bayfield admits that his menus are thought up on the day itself – which is exactly how it should be if you want to march exactly in step with the market – and they change frequently. Flavours are often more Mediterranean than Cornish, but the materials can be quite exciting. A steamed fillet of sea bass with a saffron and Chablis essence, or pasta shells filled with Vulscombe goats' cheese and wild mushrooms, served with a chilli salsa, or fresh crab with a tomato syllabub are great spins to put on Cornish cooking.

Westcountry dishes: souffléed saffron bread and butter pudding.

MAWNAN

<u>H</u>

Nansidwell

Mawnan, TR11 5HU.

12.30–13.45, 19.00–21.30.

Annual closure: 2–31 Jan.

☎ 01326 250340; fax 01326 250440.

🚪 from A39, take A394 to Helston, after 1 mile follow sign to Mabe and Mawnan Smith.

((((£33.

🛏 £76.

🛏 £99.

Banks of mullioned windows look over lawns to the water beyond. 'Civilized', 'restful', 'beautiful', are some of the epithets heard about this country house and its hospitality. Anthony Allcott's cooking is match to the architecture, in a style that compares to many such places across the country. Materials, if not recipes, are steadfastly local and immediate. He has a way with fish – useful, given the location – and examples like John Dory with Helford mussels on a prawn and brandy sauce or monkfish with Helford oysters and oranges make good use of what's to hand. There is also a good choice of Westcountry cheeses.

MAXWORTHY
FARMHOUSE B&B
Wheatley Farm
Maxworthy, PL15 8LY.
🍴**April–Oct.**
Annual closure: Nov–Mar.
☎ **01566 781232.**
🍴🍴 £11 (unlicensed).
🗝 £40.

Handsome bedrooms here in the Griffins' farm, and good farmhouse cookery that draws on the locality for its ingredients in dishes such as lamb steak topped with breadcrumbs and cheese, roast beef from South Devons, salmon cooked with cream, and in heady country puddings such as brambly pie, crumbles and a decent junket.

Westcountry dishes: pork in cider and honey.

MITHIAN
P
Miners Arms
Mithian, TR26 0QU.
🍴**12.00–14.30, 18.30–21.30.**
☎ **01872 582375.**
🍴🍴 £12.

This is a pub that might win an 'I Spy' contest: wall paintings, old plaster work, a 'penance cupboard' (I am still unsure what that was for), old wainscoted rooms, a secret tunnel, and a ghost: it has every oddity a pub could need. Best of all, the fish is as fresh as a daisy and worth returning for. The menu is never large, but that is often an indicator of freshness. Good pub cookery.

Westcountry dishes: **Crab bake.**

MOUSEHOLE
<u>R</u>

Cornish Range

6 Chapel Street, Mousehole, TR19 6SB.
(♨)**Sunday lunch, 19.00–21.00 Thurs–Sat (winter),**
19.00–21.30 Mon–Sat (summer).
☎ **01736 731488.**
(♨)(♨) **£22.50.**

Pine beams, chairs, tables, mantels and dressers give a certain unity of tone to this cheerful restaurant that is home to, yes, an old-fashioned range of fair dimensions: black, brass and polish. Seafood is another reason to call. Several ways to deal with crab are explored in a weekly menu that suggests it for stuffing smoked salmon parcels, or served under a hot cheese sauce on a bed of spinach, as well as offering other good fish such as tuna, cod, sole, and monkfish. On a Valentine's Day menu, there are Helford oysters; but only on that day – aphrodisiacs must have prompted the thought. We tend to forget that Helford oysters are the best natives in the country and yet are surprisingly difficult to locate in their region of origin. Chefs and restaurateurs will often protest (with reason) that the customers do not order them, and they are not cheap enough to chuck away. So a local resource goes to waste. It is easier to find oysters in London than it is in Cornwall. A contributory factor in England's culinary difficulties has been the conservatism and prejudice of the consumers. Like the chicken and the egg, it is not easy to determine which party causes the under-performance of the other, but I do know that such wonderful oysters would not go unnoticed in France, or Spain or other European country.

Westcountry dishes: **The Cornish Range fish pie (Newlyn fish, prawns and mushrooms in dill cream sauce).**

MOUSEHOLE
H
Old Coastguard Inn
The Parade, Mousehole, TR19 7PR.
12.00–14.30, 18.00–21.30.
☎ 01736 731222; fax 01736 731720.
£24.50.
 £25.
£50.

Nanterrow cheese with olive salad is a light meal offered at this hotel with a view over waves tumbling on to headlands. It captures well the melding of local and foreign that is possible, creating a new hybrid. Perhaps fish is the best item to pursue on the menus available in bar or restaurant. Nothing has to come from very far away, and it benefits from freshness and variety.

Westcountry dishes: **Cornish junket and strawberries.**

MYLOR
P
Pandora Inn
Restronguet Creek, Mylor, TR11 5ST.
12.00-14.30, 19.00-21.30 .
Annual closure: Christmas Day.
☎ 01326 372678.
£26.

Directions to the inn are as detailed for sailors as they are for drivers; we're in yachtie country. There is also a pontoon with showers and fresh water where boats can moor overnight. A number of dishes in the restaurant, though less in the bar, might lead you to believe we were in Thai waters – prawn wontons with a Thai salad, or strips of chicken in sherry and coconut cream sauce – and remember the inn was named after a ship sent to Tahiti in pursuit of the Bounty mutineers. The building and low-ceilings are all-English, as are the cream teas served on the pontoon come the afternoon, and so too is the excellent crab and seafood that can be had in any number of ways, from sandwiches to tarts to pies, or plainly cooked and savoured for itself.

Westcountry dishes: **Restronguet fish pie.**

PADSTOW
R (WITH ROOMS)
Seafood Restaurant
Riverside, Padstow, PL23 8BY.
12.00-14.00, 19.00-22.00 (Mon-Sat).
☎ **01841 532485; fax 01841 533344.**
£45.
£46.
£88.

The national enthusiasm for Rick Stein's television cookery has been impressive, but the same applause has been heard from the massed ranks of customers at the Seafood for several years before he ever appeared on screen. The reasons are the same: immense energy, commitment to the raw material, encouragement of local suppliers, and ability to make a place hum with enjoyment. Some of this is due to Jill Stein's natural sense of hospitality, transmitted to all the staff; the rest to Rick and his kitchen team's skill at the stove. Fish, thought boring or anticlimactic by a large segment of Britain's population, is made quite the opposite at the Seafood. The cooking takes the world as its inspiration, even if the raw material is usually from Cornwall: mackerel gets chilli and ginger, haddock spring onion mash and morel mushrooms. But the fish wins through, whatever the flavours grafted on to it, and a visit here is a must-do. The restaurant will be closed at the beginning of 1998 for a major refurbishment.

Westcountry dishes: **Sea bass and samphire; grilled lobster; Dover sole with sea salt and lime.**

PADSTOW
H

St Petrocs

4 New Street, Padstow, PL28 8EA.

⏱**12.30–14.00, 19.00–22.00 (Tues–Sat).**
Annual closure: 21–31 Dec.
☎ **01841 532700; fax 01841 532942.**

 on one way system leading out of Padstow town centre.

🍴🍴 **£26.95.**
🛏 **£33.**
🛎 **£68.**

※

This handsome hotel is Rick Stein's second venture in the town. While peace may reign in the rooms upstairs, the bistro pounds to its own rhythm: busy it certainly is. A set-price menu offers plenty of choice, with fish getting fair treatment, but not the heavy emphasis of the Seafood. The style of cookery is as robust and creative as the parent's, although the species of fish represented may inhabit the lower end of the price spectrum. Chargrilled grey mullet with slivers of garlic, chilli and olive oil, or calf's liver with sage, Parma ham, olive oil mashed potato and roasted onions are two dishes that might give a clue to the manner of cooking. Stick around for a lemon or a chocolate tart. Service is cheerful and competition for seats pretty intense. If you have no time for a full meal, Rick Stein can provide for your picnic at his delicatessen, or lighter meals next door.

PENANCE

PENZANCE
<u>H</u>
Tarbert Hotel
Clarence Street, Penzance, TR18 2NU.
19.00–20.30.
Annual closure: 23 Dec–30 Jan.
☎ **01736 363758.; fax 01736 331336.**
£18.
£28.
£48.

How many readers eat bison sausages flavoured with green peppercorns every day? You can try them at the Evans' small hotel, once a sea-captain's house. Not very Cornish, but balance them with hog's pudding, which is, or local goats' cheese wrapped in bacon, or Menallack Cheddar cheese from the choice of British cheeses at the end of the meal. There is a daily fish menu, giving an opportunity sometimes to eat black bream, something almost as uncommon as bison. That is caught on their doorstep.

Westcountry dishes: pork in cider.

PENZANCE
<u>R</u>
Ward's
12–13 Chapel Street, Penzance, TR18 4AW.
12.00–14.15, 19.00–21.30.
☎ **01736 363540.**
£12 lunch, £18 Dinner.

Alan and Sue Ward changed the name of this restaurant from Richmond's at the beginning of 1997. A seasonal menu lays down the main outline of their style: a little bit of this country and that, in the modern British manner, and those in search of local food would best enquire about the daily fish supplies.

PHILLEIGH
<u>P</u>
Roseland Inn

Philleigh, TR2 5NB.

🍴12.00–14.15, 19.00–21.00.

☎ 01872 580254; fax 01872 580951.

🚪 between the A3078 to St Mawes and the King
Harry ferry.

🍴🍴 £10.

The inn is a little bower of flowers with baskets, roses and
trellised fencing are all a-bloom. The food is robustly in
British country, but what marks the Roseland out from
others in the district is the quality of fish delivered to its
door. Try the seafood extravaganza, or plump for 'Philleigh
angels' which are fresh scallops with smoked bacon, cooked
in garlic butter. Beef stew comes, in Devon and Cornwall
style, with herby dumplings.

PHILLEIGH
<u>R</u>
Smugglers Cottage

Tolverne, Philleigh, TR2 5NG.

🍴10.30–17.30.

Annual closure: Nov–May.

☎ 01872 580309; fax 01872 580216.

🚪 1/2 mile from the King Harry Ferry on the
Philleigh side.

🍴🍴 £14.00.

American troops used the cottage and foreshore to embark
for D-Day in 1944. There is no need to take a visit quite so
seriously, leave the bazooka at home, but you can arrive
here, even today, by boat from Falmouth. During their
long tenure, the Newmans have seen the pattern of trade
change quite a bit. At present, they offer plenty of food and
refreshment all through the day, with a buffet at lunchtime.
Pasties are either steak, or vegetable, or cheese and onion.
There is venison sausage hotpot, chicken and ham pie, egg

and bacon pie, fish pie, ploughman's lunch with Cornish cheeses, and masses of cakes and puddings all served with clotted cream. Cream teas are an essential afternoon pastime.

Westcountry dishes: Cornish pasties; crab tart.

POLPERRO
R
Kitchen
The Coombes, Polperro, PL13 2RQ.
🍴19.00–21.30, Mon–Sat.
☎ 01503 272780.
🍴🍴 £20.

The Batesons' well packed restaurant seems to lead a double life in cookery-speak. On the one hand there is the fish, fresh from the harbour (or not so far away) that will appeal to many of those who come to the South West for just that pleasure. And on the other is a long menu of Asian, Indian and other cuisines that must add the spice of life to Polperro's culinary palette.

Westcountry dishes: sole in scrumpy; Cornish crab bisque; smoked fish platter.

PORTLOE
R (WITH ROOMS)
Tregain
Portloe, TR2 5QU.
🍴10.00–17.30, all week; from 19.00, Mon–Sat.
Annual closure: Nov–Mar.
☎ 01872 501252.
🍴🍴 £25 (dinner).
🛏 £19.
🛏 £38.

Perhaps it should be a set for the next Daphne du Maurier film: the lane goes down to the sea and opposite the church is Tregain. A long cottage, with tables outside for sunny days, and Clare Holdsworth at the stove from morning till night during the season. In the day, much less substantial food may be had than in the evening, but people should stop for toasted saffron buns with honey, or a full cream tea or the pasties made at the Del Beer Bakery in St Mawes. Come dinner time, fish is the main attraction: crab, scallops, lobster (to order), fresh sea bass with saffron and mustard seed, and always a crab soup and a fish soup. Clare Holdsworth is a true enthusiast.

RUAN HIGH LANES
H
Hundred House Hotel
Ruan High Lanes, TR2 5JR.
🍴19.30.
Annual closure: Nov–Feb.
☎ **01872 501336; fax 01872 501151.**
▣ **take A3078 to St Mawes; hotel is 4 miles beyond Tregony on right hand side, just before Ruan High Lanes.**
🍴🍴 £25.
🛏 £36.
🛏 £72.

Plumb in the middle of Roseland Peninsula, the hotel, brightly painted cream, surrounded by gardens and sheltering hedge, is well placed to receive the best of the Cornish harvest, be it cheese from Menallack Farm in Treverva (where they also sell produce from other Cornish growers, makers and farmers), or mackerel from the smokehouses at Charlestown to make fine food that joins 'good' and 'home' together to make 'cookery'. Kitty Eccles soaks grapefruit with Cornish mead to made a Westcountry variant on the routine; she offers lots of fish – on the principle, perhaps, that visitors come from fish-starved towns in middle England; and she is not averse to blowing local trumpets when, for instance, the plum harvest delivers Kea plums

from Trelissick. This variety is not dissimilar to Dittisham
plums in Devon (see the entry for Fingals in that county).
A steam pudding is the result, or maybe a plum and orange
soufflé.

Westcountry dishes: **Kea plum steamed pudding.**

ST AUSTELL
H
Boscundle Manor.
Tregrehan, St Austell, PL25 3RL.
🍴**19.30–20.30 (but residents only on Sun).**
Annual closure: end of October–Easter.
☎ **01726 813557; fax 01726 814997.**
🚗 **2 miles E of St Austell, off A390, signposted**
Tregrehan.
🍴🍴 **£27.50.**
🛏 **£65.**
🛏 **£110.**

Ruins of Wheal Eliza tin mine are above the house which
itself is far from ruinous. To judge from some descriptions
of visits to Andrew and Mary Flint's sumptuous conversion
and renovation of this property on the extreme outskirts of
St Austell (home of the china clay industry) it is the baths
that catch the eye: spas or Jacuzzis everywhere. A sense of
being in someone's home, perhaps the ultimate aim of small
English country hotels, may extend to the dining-room,
where Mary Flint cooks dream dinner parties. The menu is
kept short but ample, with two or three choices in each
course, finishing with Quicke's Cheddar, a Yarg or a local
goats' cheese. Fish is worth pursuit: shellfish a frequent
item in the summer, and how many of us can regularly pro-
pose a meal with sea bass and turbot in succeeding courses?
It being Cornwall, cream is rarely missing, be it cheesecake
made with clotted cream or sauces on a cream base.

Westcountry dishes: **fillet of pork with apples, cider and**
cream.

ST HILARY
FARM B&B
Ennys

St Hilary, TR20 9BZ.

🍴19.00.

Annual closure: Christmas week.

☎ **01736 740262.**

🚗 **signed from the B3280 N of Goldsithney.**

🍴🍴 **£17.50 (unlicensed).**

🛏 **£35.**

🛏 **£45.**

More comfort than farmyard, but the pigs, goats and calves are real enough, though visitors may savour them from the poolside rather than squeezing on the Wellingtons. 'The mother of all breakfasts' was one journalist's dictum, but after a day's wind surfing, fishing, walking or exploration, there'll be room enough for dinner, which Susan White produces from her slate-floored kitchen with an Aga. Try persuading her to bake a pasty for a picnic, or hevva cake for tea, or Cornish splits if hunger really bites. Otherwise, be content with a bake of scallops, megrim (this is a flat fish caught off Ireland – used for stews in Boulogne, we are told, where the fishermen called it not very politely salope), prawns and crab, or pork tenderloin with coriander and cream as centrepieces to excellent meals.

Westcountry dishes: **Cornish pasties; sugar-glazed gammon in cider; Cornish splits; hevva (heavy) cake.**

ST IVES
<u>H</u>
Garrack Hotel

Burthallan Lane, Higher Ayr, St Ives, TR26 3AA.
🍴19.00–20.30.
☎ 01736 796199; fax 01736 798955.
🚍 **reached from the B3306 St Ives–Zennor road; or**
follow signs to Porthmeor Beach and Car Parks.
🍴🍴 £25.00.
🛏 £61.50.
🛏 £88.00.

There is a live tank for lobsters at this family-run hotel looking over the surfing beach at Porthmeor. Benjamin Reeve will cook them however you want. Being so near to Newlyn, Cornwall's most important fishing port, means that fish is of the freshest and perhaps the most exciting ingredient. The style of cooking is lively and abreast of current fashion, though tradition rules for sweets when every day another English hot pudding is produced to accompany the redoubtable trolley. The wine list includes three Cornish items, from the Camel Valley and Polmassick.

ST IVES
<u>R</u>
Pig 'n' Fish

Norway Lane, St Ives, TR26 1LZ.
🍴12.30-13.45, 19.00-21.30 (Tues-Sat).
Annual closure: Nov-Feb.
☎ 01736 794204.
🍴🍴 £26.50.

The name of the restaurant might be a shorthand description of Cornish cookery as a whole. Paul Sellars worked for some years with Rick Stein at the Seafood in Padstow. His style is often comparable, in that he takes the best that Cornwall can offer, by way of fish, and uses recipes and methods garnered from around the world to convert it to something quite novel and appetizing. New-wave fish cookery is not so strident as to mask the true flavour of the flesh, but it does put a different angle on it. Megrim sole with green ginger, spring onions and a soya butter sauce, or monkfish with couscous and red peppers or a warm mussel salad with parsley pesto are three instances of ways to make an old dog dance. This restaurant is a good reason for going to the Tate Gallery at St Ives.

ST KEYNE

H

Well House

St Keyne, PL14 4RN.

🍴 12.30–14.00, 19.00–21.00 .

☎ 01579 342001; fax 01579 343891.

🚗 signed to St Keyne well from village.

🍴🍴 £31.50.

🛏 £65.

🛏 £95.

Nick Wainford's small country-house hotel is a model of sophisticated understatement, yet utter comfort everywhere. A meal is in the mainstream of modern British cookery, which means that while the combinations and methods reflect professional practice, and the flavours often import sunbeams from other countries, it is rooted in what is available in the immediate vicinity. Fish is top quality (from Looe), and something quite humble will be given a lift of skill and ingenuity, whether a first course of mixed roast fish with vegetable fettucine, or a main dish of rabbit stuffed with a rabbit confit and studded with wild mushrooms. Noisettes of pork topped with an apple and sage mousseline is another typical transformation of what at home would be pork chops with apple sauce and a bit of sage. The cheeseboard is entirely Westcountry; as Nick Wainford comments, 'We now have over sixty cheeses to choose from.'

ST MAWES

R

Broomers Restaurant.

14 Marine Parade, St Mawes, TR2 5DW.

10.00–17.00, 19.00–21.30 (Apr–Sept; closed Sun dinner and Mon, Oct–Mar)

Annual closure: Jan–Feb, closed during the day

☎ 01326 270411.

 £21 (dinner).

The smart little restaurant is just the place to sit and watch the goings-on in the harbour. Hours are extended in summer months, and visitors welcomed all through the day for snacks and teas, as well as Cornish hevva (heavy) cake, which is a fruit slice that originally used suet or lard as well as butter or cream. Pasties too, 'Meat and veg with a crusty edge', are on the board. Keith Ives was Savoy-trained, and knows good fish when he sees it. The materials supplied by 'Scruff' O'Toole off the boats in the Bay are matchless.

Westcountry dishes: St Mawes Bay scallops; Cornish pasty; Cornish cream tea.

TIDEFORD

R

Heskyn Mill

Tideford, PL12 5JS.

12.00–14.00, 18.45–21.45 (Tues–Sat).

☎ 01752 851481.

🚌 turn off A38 at St Germans, turn immediate right under road bridge.

 £28.

The visitor is in no doubt that it's a mill: the machinery remains on full view in this nicely secluded site, a short hop from the main road from Plymouth. Frank Eden tries his hand at many national styles: a chicken satay may sit next to

Mexican spiced lamb or Cajun grilled fish. But those in search of Westcountry foods could do no better than try some of his meat dishes, particularly those based on wild (not farmed) venison, or local game.

Westcountry dishes: pheasant breast cooked with apples and Somerset apple brandy; honey-glazed rack of Cornish lamb.

TREBURLEY

<u>P</u>

Springer Spaniel

Treburley, PL15 9NS.

📍 **12.00–14.00, 18.30–21.00.**

☎ **01579 370424; fax 01566 783254.**

🚌 **on the A388 between Launceston and Callington.**

📍📍 **£17.50.**

This pub, where guests can warm their toes before a glowing wood stove, won the accolade of Cornish Dining Pub of the Year from the Good Pub Guide. Either bar meals or something more elaborate in the restaurant will demonstrate the reason. Those in search of Cornish food should investigate the crab and leek pasties, remembering that leeks were as popular a vegetable in the South West as they ever were in Wales – think of likky pie, another Cornish standby. The bacon and egg tart is now composed to be more digestible, something along the lines of a quiche, but earlier recipes used to call for a pastry bottom to be covered with bacon, eggs were broken on top of that, then more bacon and finally a pastry cover. It would keep out cold weather, but reminds me of a spectacularly rich Cornish way with fried eggs, which was to give each of them a hat of clotted cream. Talk about gut-busting!

Westcountry dishes: Cornish crab and leek pasty; bacon and egg tart.

TRESCO, ISLES OF SCILLY
H

Island Hotel

Tresco, Isles of Scilly, TR24 0PU.

⑪ **12.00-14.15, 18.45-21.30.**

Annual closure: Nov-Feb.

☎ **01720 422883; fax 01720 423008.**

⑪⑪ **£35.**

🛏 **incl. dinner, £75.**

🛏 **incl. dinner, £150.**

The instructions are to take the helicopter from Penzance, but you could come by sea – and then be met by tractor and trailer. What you cannot do is walk here from anywhere. However you arrive, the welcome is enthusiastic, and the food enthusiastically Scillonian. Much, of course, has to be shipped expensively from the mainland, but the visitor is well advised to explore the fish and shellfish that is here in abundance on most days through the season. Failing lobster or crab, there is Devon beef. They are to be congratulated on their wide choice of Westcountry cheeses.

TRESILLIAN
R(WITH ROOMS)
Manor Cottage

Tresillian, TR2 4BN.

19.30–22.00 Thurs–Sat .

Annual closure: 2 weeks Nov.

☎ **01872 520212.**

£23.50.

£17.

£32.

Carlton Moyle loves saffron, and to that extent is in touch with Cornish roots. John Dory with saffron and spinach or toasted apricot and saffron pudding are two examples. Saffron cake is a third. Saffron cake in Cornwall was originally yeast-raised, as were all such cakes, with spices and fruit as well as the golden hue of saffron. There is a set-price menu with plenty of choice served in the conservatory-like adjunct to this small Georgian house, and it offers some nice combinations of ingredients, for instance crab tart with a tomato vinaigrette or seafood sausage with a lemon vinaigrette, as well as items not often found in restaurant kitchens. Salt cod is one example: common in Latin countries, but rare in Britain. Yet it all came from the cod banks of Newfoundland, exploited and colonized by sailors of the South West, then exported to Latin countries (from whom we took port wine as fair trade). Mr Moyle serves it with a parsleyed potato salad and a light chilli sauce: a manner perhaps more familiar to Spaniards than Cornishmen, but appetizing.

Westcountry dishes: John Dory with saffron and spinach; Saffron cake.

TRURO

<u>H</u>

Alverton Manor

Tregolls Road, Truro, TR1 1XQ.
🍽 **11.45–13.45, 19.00–21.30.**
☎ **01872 76633; fax 01872 222989.**
🍽🍽 **£16 (lunch), £25 (dinner).**
🛏 **£63.**
🛏 **£99.**

There is no more perfect Gothic cathedral that Truro's and it was built in the 1860s, not so long before the Sisters of the Epiphany took up residence in the buildings housing this hotel. Monastic, it is not. Acres of fabric and the sweet comfort of deep-tissue cushioning make sure of that. Perhaps the proposed health complex and swimming pool will count as modern asceticism. The ecclesiastical air has not entirely faded, though now overlaid by crimson and gilt, in the former chapel which is billed as 'the ultimate venue' for your product launch, fashion show or banquet. Colin Gilbert's style of cooking is resolutely modern, exemplified in dishes like asparagus and scallops with crispy aubergine and a coriander and chilli salsa, but there is Cornish fish to be had – try the seafood platter when available.

Westcountry dishes: Cornish smoked eel with mussels; hogs' pudding.

Devon

Introduction

'The squab pye, the herb pye, the leek and pork pye, on which clouted cream was profusely poured – the goose and parsnip, and the fish and apple pye were frequent,' wrote the Devon antiquary Richard Polwhele in his *Recollections,* published about the time of Waterloo. Placing the pie at the forefront of Devon's cookery is no accident. So much food of the South West was wrapped or encased in pastry, taking us back to medieval practice where food was baked in 'coffins' of thick pastry in wood-fired bread ovens rather than in flan dishes or pie moulds as we do today.

Devon is England's third biggest county. Two coasts, two moors, deep coombs, lush pasture in broad river valleys, cereal growing uplands, sheep walks, forest and woodland are all here, presenting a large and varied palette on which to paint a local gastronomy.

Industry has played its part as well: tin mining along the southern edge of Dartmoor, quarrying and china clay, woollen processing and cloth making, paper making and ship building conspired to make the county as rich as any other in early modern England. Some survive, but have been overtaken by tourism and retirement, with their dependent services, as the chief preoccupation of many.

The land yields its tithe of produce and foodstuffs, but the coasts' rich harvest of fish and shellfish is perhaps the most prized at Devon's tables – by strangers if not the inhabitants themselves. 'Local' cookery often means fish cookery, although an evening meal in a Dartmoor farm-house will bring you back to the earth, not the sea.

Tourism has had a beneficial effect on all sorts of cater-ing, though many would have once said the consequence was dire. There is perhaps a greater concentration of good cooks plying for hire in this county than in any outside London. The range of places is great, from the luxurious country-house hotel to small farm that grows and nurtures its own food: one reason why Devon is the county where locality is most emphasized.

Some local dishes:

Squab pie
Junket
Chudleighs
Dartmouth pie
Devon flats
Clotted cream
Likky stew
Parsley dumplings
Apple cake
Apple in and out pudding
Exeter stew
Devonshire stew
Honiton fairings
Mazzard tart
Potato cakes
White pot

ASHBURTON
B&B
Gages Mill

Buckfastleigh Road, Ashburton, TQ13 7JW.
(🍴)19.00.
Annual closure: mid-Nov–Feb.
☎ 01364 652391.
🚪 on the old A38 between Ashburton and
Buckfastleigh.
(🍴)(🍴) £17.50.
🛏 £22.
🛏 £44.

The Mill, spick and span on wide lawns, lies just beyond
the town, the Devon Expressway within sight but out of
hearing. It was once a woollen mill, not corn, and the big
mills at Buckfastleigh still remind the visitor that this part
of Devon was a powerhouse of the English wool trade. The
tradition of stock production, for wool or meat, has lingered
and the Moores' dinners reflect how well supplied is the
Ashburton district, for instance by Tom Lang the butcher
(who has one of the few small slaughterhouses left in the
area after their decimation by over-regulation in recent
years), or by Tordean Farm at Rattery who produce
organically reared meat, and by Deer Force 10 just up the
road at Holne, who farm venison. Dinners at the Mill are
three-course, without choice, but taking into account the
preferences of that night's guests. Annie Moore might cook
potato cakes with Dartmouth smoked salmon, pork fillet in
cider with apples and onion and a full plate of vegetables –
broccoli, cottage cheese and chives, broad beans and bacon,
mashed potatoes – then finish it all with a chocolate parfait.
The advantage of a no-choice meal is that the cook can seize
what's good that day in the shops or the market. No need
for a supply wagon to call every two weeks to stock the
freezer.

ASHBURTON
H

Holne Chase

Two Bridges Road, Ashburton, TQ13 7NS.
🍽 12.00–14.00, 19.15–21.00.
☎ 01364 631471; fax 01364 631453.
🚍 3 miles NW of Ashburton on A384.
🍽🍽 £26 (lunch), £31 (dinner).
🛏 £60.
🛎 £115.

The original owners used this as a sporting retreat: lord
knows how big their main house was. What was once a
weekend cottage now accommodates a sizable country hotel
which affords a different, but equally satisfying, escape from
the rush of life. Set in a wide hollow between crags and
forest, the terrace looks over a massive lawn. A shaded walk
descends to the Dart, where fish jump and water splashes
from mirrored pool to mirrored pool. On the way, you pass
the walled garden, with serried ranks of vegetables. You
think of dinner, which steadily improves in quality as the
Hughes, who have not been here long, get better settled in.
The force that drives them is local materials and garden
produce. The treatment accorded them is outward-looking,
not constrained by tradition, but the use of what comes to
hand in any particular season is a vital ingredient of a
developing local cuisine.

Westcountry dishes: a salad of Dorset crab and Brixham
scallop with pimento and lime; rhubarb crème brûlée with
nougat and strawberry syrup; windfall apples filled with
their own ice-cream and an apple and cider turnover.

ASHMILL
FARMHOUSE B&B.
Kerscott Farm
Ashmill, EX36 4QG.

🍴 **18.30 (residents only).**

☎ **01769 550262.**

🚗 **6 miles E of South Molton, off the A361 on the B3227 road to Bampton.**

🍴🍴 **£8.**

🛏 **£18.**

🛏 **£36.**

Theresa Sampson's hospitality has won her the award for the best farmhouse bed and breakfast in the country from the AA. It must be the cream – or perhaps the butter she used to churn from her house-cow's milk. Take a normal breakfast at Kerscott: sausages from their own pigs, eggs from their chickens, local potatoes and tomatoes, Theresa's bread, Theresa's jams and preserves, and laver when it's available in Barnstaple market. And dinner: Ruby Red beef, their own; pork, coated with breadcrumbs and herbs, with a cider, apple and honey sauce (the hives on their ground too). When we asked her to name some of her suppliers, Theresa mentioned the W.I. stall in South Molton market: a group of like-minded people, making the best of their locality. (It is worth a note that the now celebrated food and recipe writer Geraldene Holt first cut her culinary teeth making cakes for the W.I. in Tiverton.) Kerscott is a flower-covered old farmhouse – four inglenooks – on the southern reaches of Exmoor. There is much cooking to explore, as well as countryside to walk and ride in. Bookmark the squab pie, another famous Devon dish. Although the name may imply it was once made with baby pigeons, the squab seems only to refer to chops of collops of meat, usually pork, although sometimes (as in the Dartmouth variant) mutton.

Westcountry dishes: squab pie (pork, apple, cream filling in savoury pastry); trout with butter and parsley sauce; Exmoor lamb hot pot with herby dumplings; steamed kale with poached eggs on top, sprinkled with cheese.

ASHPRINGTON

<u>P</u>

Watermans Arms

Bow Bridge, Ashprington, TQ9 7EG.

🍽 **12.00–14.30, 18.30–21.30 .**

☎ **01803 732214.**

🚗 **on lane between Totnes and Tuckenhay.**

🍽🍽 **£10.00.**

🛏 **£36.**

🛏 **£70.**

When I first came to the Westcountry more than twenty years ago, I was immediately directed to the Watermans. Its ploughman's lunch was famous then, as well as its situation and happy rural atmosphere. In the intervening years, many thousands have trod the same path, and it continues to meet their expectations, although the scale of the things has grown enormously.

ASHWATER

<u>H</u>

Blagdon Manor

Ashwater, EX21 5DF.

🍽 **20.00.**

Annual closure: Christmas, February.

☎ **01409 211224; fax 01409 211634.**

🚗 **off A388 Launceston to Holsworthy, second junction (driving north) signed to Ashwater, then road signed to Blagdon.**

🍽🍽 **£22.50.**

🛏 **£60.**

🛏 **£95.**

Like a yokel in silk knickers, Blagdon Manor may be an ancient farmhouse, but once through the door, the transformation into cocoon of luxury (or at the very least extreme comfort) is impressive. Fresh-air fiends can frolic in the grounds to enhance an appetite that would be very jaded to resist Gill Casey's cookery. Dinner is taken on a giant stretch of communal mahogany and stints nothing over three courses. Salmon sits on a bed of champ (a mixture of potatoes, peas and onions, from Northern Ireland); beef Wellington comes with a potato and parsnip bake; and there's a brandy butter ice-cream with red fruits poached in spiced wine. After that, who's for croquet?

BAMPTON
H
Bark House Hotel.

Oakford Bridge, Bampton, EX16 9HZ.
🍽 **12.15–13.50 (light lunches), 19.15.**
Annual closure: 3–31 Jan, 1 week in March.
☎ **01398 351236.**
🚗 **8 miles N of Tiverton, on A396, between Tiverton and Bampton.**
🍽🍽 **£23.00.**
🛏 **£24.50.**
🛏 **£49.50.**

The fact that this building once housed a tannery accounts for the name. Today, the hotel nestles against the hillside, with terraced gardens climbing the slope to the trees (whose bark provided the tannin) behind. Alastair Kameen has but recently taken possession of Bark House. Refurbishment complete, he cooks a country-modern menu which nods to our enjoyment of sweet-sour combinations (plum and raisin chutney served with chicken liver and apple brandy pâté), to our love of a bit of stodge at the end (steamed apricot sponge pudding with butterscotch sauce), and to the magpie tendency of British cookery (banana curry soup). Westcountry gets a look-in with lots of Exmoor venison (casseroled with port and mushrooms), meat dishes with substance (lamb's kidney, thyme and parsley pudding), and a board loaded with local cheeses.

Westcountry dishes: steamed fillets of brill with a dill cream sauce; apple tart with apple brandy sabayon; crab and mixed lettuce salad with cider vinegar dressing.

BANTHAM
<u>B&B</u>
Widcombe House

Bantham, TQ7 3AA.
📞19.30–20.30.
Annual closure: Nov–Jan.
☎ **01548 561084.**
🚌 **first building on left, 1.5 miles towards Bantham from Bantham Cross on A379.**
🛏 £24.
🛏 £44.

After many years working in city kitchens, Jill Hutcheson has finally achieved her ambition of growing her own fruit and vegetables, not just buying them in a supermarket. Her nightly dinners revolve around local suppliers such as Riverford Farm at Staverton who grow organic vegetables and rear organic pork as well as selling other meats and making sausages and bacon, or Ticklemore Cheese Shop in Totnes who supply the best of Westcountry cheeses, or smoked fish from Kingsbridge. The meals are unpretentious in concept, but conceal much care and attention to fine detail.

Westcountry dishes: pork with cider.

BARNSTAPLE
<u>R (WITH ROOMS)</u>
Lynwood House

Bishops Tawton Road, Barnstaple, EX32 9EF.
📞12.00–14.00, 19.00–21.30 (Mon–Sat).
☎ **01271 343695; fax 01271 379340.**
📞📞 £25.
🛏 £47.50.
🛏 £67.50.

This is a long-established family-run restaurant which has forged close links with its suppliers over the years, as well as welcoming holidaymakers and other guests from one season to the next. It stands to reason that many people come here for the fish. Just as we have all now read or seen Rick Stein, so Lynwood House is no slouch in methods of fish cookery, with lively foreign flavours being introduced from the Mediterranean or further afield. There may, of course, be danger that we will soon only cook our fine cold-water species with lime or coriander, or chilli and coconut, just as once upon a time we would smother them in yucky flour-based sauces, but the Roberts seem to be holding a balance between what is today's adventure, and the plainer cookery that lets the fish speak loudly for itself.

Westcountry dishes: skate with brown butter; Dover sole with butter and parsley.

BISHOP'S TAWTON
H
Halmpstone Manor
Bishop's Tawton, EX32 0EA.
19.00–21.00.
Annual closure: Nov & Jan.
☎ **01271 830321; fax 01271 830826.**
🚌 **2 miles from Bishop's Tawton towards Chittlehampton.**
£40.
£70.
£100.

There is a working farm, but the house is so magnificent you would be forgiven for thinking it a pleasure-dome, no place of daily grind. The Stanburys have decorated and furnished to the last inch: four-posters keep sleepers snug, graciousness rules elsewhere. Jane Stanbury cooks a five-course dinner each night, with a proper fish course after the soup, and cheese as a matter of routine. The supply lines mean much of the meat, fish and vegetables come from the hotel's doorstep: eat partridge, Devon beef or lamb with confidence.

BOVEY TRACEY
<u>H</u>

Edgemoor

Haytor Road, Bovey Tracey, TQ13 9LE.

🍴12.00–14.00, 19.00–21.00.

Annual closure: New Year.

☎ **01626 832466; fax 01626 834760.**

🚪 **on road from Bovey Tracey to Haytor and Widecombe.**

🍴🍴 £24.25.

🛏 £42.50.

🛏 £75.

Here's a cossetted place to rest the weary limbs after a hard day's letter-boxing across Dartmoor. Dinners, and lunches for rainy days, meld into the modern British country-house manner, but also have unexpected Devon highlights. Exeter stew is a jugged stew of beef and onion with herbed dumplings. It used to be made in a sealed jug or stew-jar boiled in a larger pan. That way all the juices would be conserved, and a single pot of boiling water could cook vegetables and other things than the meat, economizing on heat and fuel. The Barnstaple Fair pears mentioned by the chef Edward Elliot were one of the dishes associated with the fair held in September. Many of these fairs had 'fairings' or other special biscuits or sweetmeats that were cooked during the days of happy celebration. The pears are stewed in port or red wine, with lemon juice and cloves. They can be stuck all over with almonds, 'hedgehog' style, once they have cooled.

Westcountry dishes: **pork with cider and apple sauce; Exeter stew; Barnstaple Fair pears.**

BRANSCOMBE
P

Masons Arms

Branscombe, EX12 3DJ.
🍽 **12.00–14.15, 19.00–21.15 bar; 19.00–21.00 restaurant.**
☎ **01297 680300; fax 10297 680500.**
🍽🍽 **£23.50.**
🛏 **£22.**
🛎 **£60.**

This pub occupies much of the village: there's the inn itself, then cottages close by have been converted to bedrooms. Atmosphere in the fourteenth-century core is there for the taking, although it can get very busy. Points to note are the meats spit-roasted on an open fire and the excellent crab supplied from the village, but there are other intersting local dishes. White pot is sometimes connected to Gloucestershire fairs or revels. A modern recipe describes a baked custard. Older recipes (not actually deriving from the West) suggest a rice pudding or a bread and butter pudding enriched with eggs, and sometimes including apples. Devonshire splits cause much agonizing among historians. Cornish splits are a form of bap or light yeasty bun. Devonshire splits are also called Chudleighs though not, it is thought, necessarily connected to that town. They can be yeasted buns, but there are alternative recipes that make them very similar to the British scone.

Westcountry dishes: Branscombe crab cakes; Devonshire crab pie; hash of lamb in cider; Devonshire white pot; Devonshire splits.

BROADHEMBURY
P
Drewe Arms

Broadhembury, EX14 0NF.
🍴 **12.00–14.00 (all week), 19.00–22.00 (Mon–Sat).**
Annual closure: 25 December.
☎ **01404 841267.**
🚪 **off A373 between Cullompton and Honiton.**
🍴🍴 **£25.**

Nigel and Kerstin Burge have turned this thatched epitome of the English country pub into Mecca for fish-eaters. Perhaps there is something here to do with Kerstin being of Swedish birth – this makes the gravad lax essential – but everything comes from the East Devon coast and day-boats, not the Baltic. A meal can be composed of lunchish cold platters of assorted shellfish, smoked salmon, and cheese, or perhaps some guaranteed authentic marinated herring. The glutton can research the wider field, trying lobsters, crab, oysters, a whole Dover sole, or a piece of turbot with unctuous hollandaise sauce. This is creative cooking in a bustling yet friendly environment.

BROADHEMBURY
FARMHOUSE B&B
Lane End Farm

Broadhembury, EX14 0LU.
☎ **01404 841563; fax 01392 882153.**
🍴 **residents only.**
🍴🍴 **£10.**
🛏 **£20.**
🛏 **£36.**

Just a step away from the pretty village of Broadhembury, this modern house is set in a mixed pasture and arable farm, with blazing flower borders to act as fence and boundary. Molly Bennett offers good home-cooking with much of it coming from the farm itself.

CHAGFORD

H

Gidleigh Park

Chagford, TQ13 8HH.

🍴 12.30–14.00, 19.00–21.00.

☎ 01647 432367; fax 01647 432574.

🚪 2 miles N of Chagford, do not approach from Gidleigh village; from Mill St fork R, to Holy St at bottom of hill, follow lane and signs.

🍴🍴 £40 (lunch), £65 (dinner).

🛏 £210 (incl. dinner).

🛏 £325 (incl. dinner).

From less than nothing, Paul and Kay Henderson have created one of Britain's best hotels. The house, a picturesque half-timbered Edwardian mansion, sprawls along a contour beneath woods that lead to Dartmoor. A stream splashes from boulder to boulder through the terraced garden that opens into a giant croquet lawn. The single-mindedness of the operation means no dust, no creases, no blemish, yet is effortless. Michael Caines' cookery is a fully paid-up member of that international club that measures achievement by stars and rosettes, but does not turn its back on locality – even if the dishes created, shall we say seabass accompanied by courgette flowers stuffed with a scallop mousse, are beyond regionalism. Materials are of the highest quality, particularly the fish, lamb, game and cheese, and if we wish to see arise a regional cuisine to compare with those being developed in France, Italy, and even Germany, it is chefs like Michael Caines who will lead us to it.

CHULMLEIGH
<u>B&B</u>
Old Bakehouse

South Molton Street, Chulmleigh, EX18 7BW.
🍴10.30–4.30 (Tues–Sat), 19.45 (residents only).
Annual closure: 2 weeks Feb.
☎ 01769 580137/580074.
🍴🍴 £12.50 (lunch), £18.70 (dinner).
🛏 £19.
🛏 £38.

Colin and Holly Burls remark that Chulmleigh (it made its money from wool in the Middle Ages) was bypassed by both the turnpike road and the railway. A long time ago, but it means the village retained its original character. This thatched merchant's house dating from the sixteenth century was converted into a bakery some time afterwards, which it remained until 1963. Today, it is open to all-comers for sandwiches, light meals, glorious cakes and cream teas when the sun is up, though in the evening the Burls cook only for residents. Their short menus are full of interest and succeed, as they state themselves (though not Devon folk at all), in imparting 'a true flavour of Devon to all our guests.' Three Devon vintages await the wine drinker, and Hancocks of South Molton supply the cider.

Westcountry dishes: Carver Doone's venison casserole; Exmoor pheasant with Somerset cider; Exmoor apple scone; scrumpy chicken; Devon apple cake; Somerset cider pork chops.

CLAWTON
<u>H</u>
Court Barn Country House

Clawton, EX22 6PS.
🍴12.00–14.00, 19.00–21.00.
Annual closure: early Jan.
☎ 01409 271219; fax 01409 271309.
🚪 on road from Clawton (on A388 2.5 m S of

Holsworthy) to N. Tamerton.
🍴🍴 (Lunch) £17.50, (Dinner) £23.00.
🛏 £30.
🛏 £60.

First item: it's no barn. The early name of the house (Victorian, but older in origin) was Court Baron, accurately reflecting manorial status. Today, it is comfortable, gracious and home to the Woods family; an oasis surrounded by gardens, putting greens and croquet lawns. Sue Wood cooks country-house dinners, four courses of substance, with no stinting. Rack of lamb with port and mushroom sauce might be brought to table with potato and onion parcels, leek soufflé, parsnip bake, buttered carrots, cauliflower and herb cheese, and duchesse potatoes. Still afloat? Follow with Nan's tipsy trifle, Clawton apple cake with clotted cream, summer pudding, brown bread ice-cream or sticky toffee pudding. That apple cake is interesting. Devon apple cakes were made with pastry. A Cornish author describes it as being made by 'filling a plate with pared apples, covering it with a round of pastry, baking it, reversing the crust, sugaring the apple and spreading it over the crust. When cold, cream is added if you've got it.' This is a sort of upside-down tart, like the French tarte tatin, where the juices from the apple and sugar soak and soften the pastry below. Dorset apple cake, by contrast was made with a sponge or light cake surrounding the apple. As so often, Devon and Cornwall cooks put pastry with whatever they could.

Westcountry dishes: Tamar salmon with watercress sauce; apple cake; whortleberry cheesecake.

COCKWOOD
P
Anchor Inn
Cockwood, EX6 8RA.
🍴 Mon–Sun 12.00–15.00 (Sun 14.30, 18.30–22.00).
☎ 01626 890203/891203.
🍴🍴 £25.

Cockwood is a little village at the mouth of the Exe, between Dawlish and Starcross. Sit at the quayside pub and watch boats, Great Western trains and sea birds, or changes in the weather. This is the place to taste Exe river oysters (Pacifics, not natives), or mussels in a hundred ways. The owners are defiantly in favour of English wine (they grow their own grapes), and the enthusiast will welcome their periodic tastings of Sharpham and other Westcountry vineyards. Who would have thought of bubble-and-squeak with a 1993 Loddiswell medium dry, as billed on a St George's Day tasting in 1996? The pub menu (people can have something simple or go for the full monty in the restaurant) goes in for a long list of variations, but the daily specials include lots of fish (not all of it swimming in local waters) and good roast lamb, or perhaps game from the Powderham Castle estate just a mile or two up the road.

Westcountry dishes: Devonshire pasty; homity pie (which is a cheese and potato pie with herbs); mussels in scrumpy; oysters and shellfish from the Exe.

COLEFORD
P
New Inn
Coleford, EX17 5BZ.
🍽12.00–14.00, 19.00–22.00.
Annual closure: 25–26 Dec.
☎ 01363 84242; fax 01363 85044.
🚗 5 miles W of Bampton on B3227 (do not go into Oakford village).
🍽🍽 £19.50.
🛏 £38.
🛏 £52.

You can imagine a thirteenth-century shepherd shouting to his mate across the hedge, 'There's that new inn down by the ford, do you want a jar?' Seven hundred years on, the pub is still called new, but the house is very old indeed, and filled with the sort of furnishings that townies reckon the epitome of country pubs. The food is less yokel-with-astraw-in-the-mouth. Tomato and basil soup, venison or wild boar sausages, beef and venison pie, sherried kidney tart, or Wembworthy cream, which is a sweet dish of blackcurrants with yoghourt and cream topping, are items which strike the eye. Good value, and good eating.

Westcountry dishes: crab soup; fish pie; pork in cider; scallops in cream, wine and herb sauce.

DALWOOD
P
Tuckers Arms
Dalwood, EX13 7EG.
🍴12.00–14.00, 19.00–21.30.
☎ 01404 881342.; fax 01404 881802.
🍴🍴 £9.95 (lunch), £15.55 (dinner)
🛏 £27.50.
🍽 £45.

Thatch on the outside, rich timbering within, and the coast is close enough to allow David Beck opportunity to indulge his love of seafood. This is the most important feature of the fast-changing specials menu that supplements bar food, sandwiches and ploughman's lunches. Add to that a line in apple pies, treacle puddings and treacle and walnut tarts, all with solid Devonshire cream, and the dream is complete.

DARTINGTON
P
Cott Inn
Dartington, TQ9 6HE.
🍴Meals 12.00–14.15 (14.30 Sun), 18.30–21.30 (19.00–21.00 Sun).
☎ 01803 863777; fax 01803 866629.
🍴🍴 £26.
🛏 £40.
🍽 £50.

There are not many places that cook stargazey pie, and fewer produce leeky or likky pie. The Cott Inn, which has been serving ale for several centuries, should be congratulated. The original stargazey was made with pilchards, when they were a staple of the south Devon fishery and great barrels of pickled and salted pilchards were prepared at Burgh Island for export to Mediterranean countries. Nowadays, mackerel are more likely. The traditional picture of a stargazey, a flat pie with the fish heads sticking out of the pastry, is quite accurate. The topping, like the pasty, was to seal the contents so the pie could be transported to work without spilling. The heads poked out the top because it was best not to detach the heads of small fish like pilchard before cooking, otherwise the flesh would lose its oils and moisture. But the heads would be put aside with the pastry before eating commenced. End of history lesson. Leeky or likky pie is another local dish. Bacon and leeks are cooked under a suet crust, then at the last minute a cream and egg filling is poured under the pastry to form a luscious binding. The Cott is full enough of history as it stands, these dietary extras are a bonus. Alongside them will be found a substantial and heartening range of dishes that give the concept 'pub food' a good name.

Westcountry dishes: stargazey pie; Devon jugged steak; leeky pie; rabbit and cider hot pot.

DARTMOUTH

R
Billy Budd's Bistro

7 Foss Street, Dartmouth, TQ6 9DW.
12.00–14.00, 19.00–22.00, Tues–Sat.
Annual closure: 4 weeks Jan/Feb, 1 week Nov.
☎ 01803 834842.
£12.00 (lunch), £22.00 (dinner).

Foss Street decks itself cheerfully for the summer: cars are kept out; baskets and tubs of flowers and plants add a splash of colour. Billy Budd of opera fame was never a Dartmouth boy, nor was Keith Belt, who cooks here. But he has been adopted over these past years, cooking sound fare, lighter at lunchtime, that satisfies locals and visitors alike. Long-term favourites have been twice-baked cheese soufflé and guinea fowl with red wine and mushrooms, along with real old-timers such as Camembert fritters with mango chutney which tie in with the bistro heritage: remember those days of check tablecloths and wax stalagmites for candlesticks? That's perhaps why there is often a buzz of happy enjoyment when the place is full of a summer's evening.

Westcountry dishes: pear and parsnip soup; roast duck with plum sauce; roast fillet of cod with parsley crust.

DARTMOUTH
R
Carved Angel

2 South Embankment, Dartmouth, TQ6 9AN.
🍴12.30–14.30 (Tues–Sun), 19.00–21.30 (Tues–Sat).
Annual closure: Christmas, 6 weeks Jan–Feb.
☎ **01803 832465; fax 01803 835141.**
🍴🍴 **£36.50 (lunch), £52.50 (dinner).**

This is one of the region's most celebrated restaurants where the happy visitor can snooze after lunch gazing at the busy yachts, crab-boats and ferries in the estuary or, when night falls, at the lights on the Kingswear side refracted in the rippling water. Joyce Molyneux has been cooking under the watchful eye on the angel for twenty years and more. Although no stranger to the dishes and cookery of nations other than Britain, she has evolved a style that is amazingly responsive to local supplies and the vagaries of the seasons. Her partner at the stove, Nick Coiley, marches to the same drumbeat. Flavours are vibrant; combinations of seasonal vegetables and meat or fish are constantly explored; herbs are deployed with panache and enthusiasm. Many hitherto neglected ingredients have been revived or introduced. Samphire gathered from the cliffs is partnered with brill or turbot; kid is roasted and served with redcurrant or rowan jelly; gooseberries, honey and saffron combined in an ethereal custard; elderflower made into wonderful fritters.

Occasionally, there is a specific revival, such as the Dartmouth pie, which was a recognized variant of the Devonshire squab pie during the last two centuries, now cooked by Joyce as a spiced mutton and fruit pie.

Westcountry dishes: prawns, crab and lobster; Dartmouth pie; clotted-cream ice-cream.

DARTMOUTH
<u>R</u>
Cutter's Bunch
33 Lower Street, Dartmouth, TQ6 9AN.
🍴19.00–22.00, Thurs–Sat (Winter); Thurs–Mon (Spring), Thurs–Tues (Summer).
Annual closure: 2 weeks Nov/Dec, 1 week Apr/May.
☎ **01803 832882.**
🍴🍴 **£22.50.**

Nick Crosley cooks enterprising items in this small bistro (the seats would never allow it to be anything else) one block away from the river front at Dartmouth. His fish stew inspired by the the Brazilian cooks of Bahia is wonderful, and his Thai recipes for shrimp parcels or a seafood pot are memorable as well. 'Chilli' could be his middle name. At the same time, fish landed by boats in the river, or over the hill at Brixham, is often cooked with ne'er a spike of chilli or bouquet of coriander in sight: plain and as it should be. For an angle on very good fresh ingredients, this place is worth a visit. The loin of lamb rolled in spinach and Denhay air-dried ham is one example, venison with red wine and honey sauce is another, duck breast with a powerful blackcurrant sauce and onion confit a third.

Westcountry dishes: lobster with Somerset cider brandy; scallops with cider.

DITTISHAM
H
Fingals

Coombe Manor Farm, Dittisham, TQ6 0JA.

🍴 **20.30–22.00 Tues–Sat (non–residents).**

Annual closure: Jan–Easter.

☎ **01803 722398; fax 01803 722401.**

🚪 **1 mile N of Dittisham on road to Cornworthy.**

🍴🍴**£29.50.**

🛏 **£40.**

🛏 **£60.**

There was a moment before the Corn Laws were repealed at
the beginning of Queen Victoria's reign when the farmers of
Britain, including south Devon, were doing very well
indeed, their market entirely protected from foreign competition. Not so good for the starving poor, but excellent for
farmers' incomes. The effect on farmhouses across the
region can be seen in valley after valley: they got new fronts,
fancy sash windows, nice staircases, a general facelift.
Rather as today, if you win on the Lottery, you rush out for
a Ferrari, a Porsche and a foreign holiday. Fingals occupies
just such a farm, tucked away in a silent valley, and very
comfortable indeed – and made more so by the efforts of
Richard Johnston, culminating in an indoor pool and an
architectural folly at the end of the garden. Allied to a
welcome as genuine as it is relaxed and the ingredients of a
successful stay are assembled. Cookery is of a piece with the
setting: good ingredients, intelligent execution in a modern
manner. It is worth asking for lobster here, he cooks it well,
and the Dittisham plum pie (or jam for breakfast) is a
celebration of a local breed of plums that was allegedly
introduced by German monks from the priory at
Cornworthy. A nonsense, really. The monks were not
German, and they were nuns anyway. There are several local
varieties of plums found in orchard districts throughout
England; they are often, like the Dittisham plum,
propagated by suckers. A similar fruit to the Dittisham
plum is found at Truro and called Kea.

Westcountry dishes: **Dittisham plum pie; smoked wild Dart salmon.**

DODDISCOMBSLEIGH

P

Nobody Inn

Doddiscombsleigh, EX6 7PS.

🍴restaurant 19.30–21.30, Tues–Sat.

Annual closure: 25–26 Dec.

☎ **01647 252394; fax 01647 252978.**

🍴🍴 £16.

🛏 £25.

🛌 £43.

This inn has built up a considerable reputation for wines with a wide-ranging list and the possibility of tasting a number of them by the glass, not forgetting Westcountry vineyards. Local beers and ciders are also available, and the food often complements local tipple. Cheeses, for example, are numbered in their tens, and they all come from the region, with some enterprising cooked dishes on offer as well, like their blue vinney soup in a bowl sculpted from a chunk of bread. It may be that Nick Borst-Smith's enthusiasm for wine makes him hypersensitive to the question of origin (after all, you don't just buy any old bottle from Bordeaux), but the food is as carefully purchased as any vintage, from places like Rocombe Farm (ice-cream), Denhay Farm (ham and cheese), Turtons (black pudding), and Doddiscombsleigh itself (honey).

DREWSTEIGNTON

R (WITH ROOMS)

Hunts Tor

Drewsteignton, EX6 6QW.

🍴19.30.

Annual closure: End Oct–end Feb.

☎ **01647 281228.**

🍴🍴 £27.50.

🛏 £40.

🛌 £60.

This is not a large restaurant: it seats eight people. Visitors, therefore, are guaranteed 100 per cent attention from the Harrisons, and there is a wealth of considered detail in both the accommodation and the cooking that makes Hunts Tor restful yet enlivening. It was described in a recent guide-book as 'a little monument to Devon produce'. Some of that, of course, is grown in their own garden, be it sorrel and other herbs, saladings or soft fruit; other ingredients come from round about, not least the all-Westcountry cheeseboard. That peculiarly West-Country fruit, the apple, figures in pork with cider and apples, or an open apple tart with clotted cream or again in chicken with a cider, garlic and cream sauce, while Denhay's air-dried ham – a commodity that has spread through the region like wildfire – surfaces as companion to roasted vegetables with pesto, or partnering poached pear in a tarragon dressing. Sue Harrison cooks a no-choice dinner, ensuring freshness and accurate buying with so small a number of guests to consider; which also means that it can be responsive to daily fluctuations in weather and supplies.

EAST BUCKLAND
R (WITH ROOMS)
Lower Pitt Restaurant
East Buckland, EX32 0TD.
🍴19.00–21.30 (Tues–Sat).
☎ 01598 760243.
🍴🍴 £25.
🛌 £35.
🛏 £60.

Sitting in the conservatory area during summer months is like those treetop platforms in African game parks: all is wonderfully clean and civilized inside but out there, through the glass, is nature red in tooth and claw. This is a restaurant in the country, and the plants are there to prove it. The kitchen goes some way to demonstrate the fact as well. Suzanne Lyons takes full advantage of the resource of Heal Farm, not many miles away. The organic pork, bacon and ham that Anne Petch has made so good are often on the

menu. Game is also a strong point. Dishes range wide
across the world for inspiration. Suzanne may have begun
cooking with provincial French recipes as a starting point,
but the produce and ingredients assert their local
affiliations.

Westcountry dishes: Heal Farm pork with local cider; game
and venison casserole.

EASTLEIGH
<u>B&B</u>
Pines at Eastleigh

Old Barnstaple Road, Eastleigh, EX39 4PA.
🍴residents only.
☎ **01271 860561; fax 01271 861248.**
🚗 **2 miles E of Bideford on the old Bideford to
Barnstaple road.**
🍴🍴 **£18.50.**
🛏 **£29.**
🛏 **£58.**

From the front of the house the eye can catch Bideford
Quay, Hartland Point and, on clearer days, Lundy Island. In
the kitchen Barry and Jenny Jones may sometimes offer
fresh plaice or mackerel from the boats of Clovelly or
Bideford, but more likely will be cooking good beef or
gammon, and finishing a satisfying meal with some
substantial English pudding or tart. Mr Honey (from
Parkham) supplies the breakfast sausages (pork and leek)
and the potatoes are invariably from Eastleigh Manor.

Westcountry dishes: Cornish pasty; Devonshire pork in
cider; apple crumble with cinnamon and raisins.

EXETER
R

Lamb's

15 Lower North Street, Exeter, EX4 3ET.
🍴12.00–14.00 (Tues–Fri), 19.00–22.00 (Tues–Sat).
**Annual closure: Christmas/Boxing Day, New Years
Day; last week Aug, first week Sept.**
☎ **01392 254269; fax 01392 431145.**
🍴🍴 **£25.**

Alison and Ian Aldridge proudly urge their Devon
affiliations: 'We are the only Exeter restaurant to be
members of Taste of the West and the Campaign for Real
Food.' Their menu, served in a split-level dining room
tucked beneath the Victorian iron viaduct that leaps the
valley below Exeter's multi-storey temple of car parking, is
eloquent of local produce from the aperitif of elderflower to
the plate of farmhouse cheeses at the end. They smoke and
cure their own fish and meat in the backyard, and will
happily tell you the precise origin of any ingredient you care
to ask about. Veal, for instance, is cheerful veal, not crated.
Wild Beef is not rounded up by the Marlboro Man, but it
did spend time grazing on the heaths of Dartmoor, not
merely chomping silage under cover. It is sold by Richard
Vines of Chagford, who specializes in rearing by slow
suckler method traditional English and Welsh beef breeds.
Ian Aldridge is something of a wine buff: his list usually
includes a couple of Westcountry vintages, and he will never
shirk giving his opinion.

Westcountry dishes: matured Dartmoor Wild Beef rump
steak on a bed of bubble and squeak with a Madeira sauce

EXETER
H
St Olaves Court

Mary Arches Street, Exeter, EX4 3AZ.
12.00–14.00, 18.30–21.30 (except Sat & Sun lunch).
Annual closure: first week Jan.
☎ **01392 217736; fax 01392 413054.**
£20 (lunch), £30 (dinner).
£53.
£63.

The garden and the mulberry tree in front of this Georgian merchant's house are always an unexpected sight in the centre of Exeter, and St Olave's has less of a bustle, more of a private-house feel to it than most city hotels. Much is due to the hospitality of the Wyatts, and the kitchen should also take credit. At lunch, there is freedom to eat as little or as lightly as required, but the modern British style is consistent throughout the day. Fish dishes like turbot with baby vegetables and a lemon and chilli oil, or meats like goose breast with parsnip (at Christmas) are lightly treated with the emphasis generally away from long, slow cooking. Sharpham Vineyard is represented on the wine list.

Westcountry dishes: terrine of Brixham Bay fish with balsamic dressing.

FENNY BRIDGES
FARMHOUSE B&B
Skinners Ash Farm

Fenny Bridges, EX14 0BH.
19.00.
☎ **01404 850231.**
driving W on the A30 Honiton–Exeter road, turn left after Greyhound Inn .
£8.
£16.
£32.

An advantage of staying on a farm is that you often know where the meat comes from. Jill Godfrey uses rare breeds raised on the farm in her kitchen, as well as the full slate of fruit and vegetables from her garden. Dinners are, by her own account, 'old fashioned', with roasts, puddings and pies, and fruit pies and crumbles to finish. Cream teas are also served, the scones home-made. The rare breeds are impressive looking beasts: there are Norfolk Horn sheep, Highland cattle, Longhorn cows, as well as British Lop pigs, and everyone can take part, collect the eggs, help in the feeding and probably muck out a few animal yards if you have nothing better to do.

GALMPTON
FARMHOUSE B&B
Burton Farm
Galmpton, Kingsbridge, TQ7 3EY.
🍴dinner, mainly for residents.
Annual closure: Christmas Day.
☎ **01548 561210.**
🍴🍴 £11.
🛏 £22.
🛏 £44.

This working dairy and sheep farm is a mile from Hope Cove, not much further from Salcombe and an ideal start for all the coastal, cliff-top walks a visitor could ever require. Anne Rossiter cooks generously, and draws on the farm for her own supplies of cream. milk and eggs, as well as some meat. If ever you need a course in how to use clotted cream in every department of the kitchen: here's where to come.

Westcountry dishes: beef casserole in beer with dumplings (made with clotted cream and herbs); Westcountry pork casserole; treacle tart.

GULWORTHY
<u>R (WITH ROOMS)</u>
Horn of Plenty
Gulworthy, PL19 8JD.

📻 **12.00–14.00 (Tues–Sun), 19.00–21.00 .**

Annual closure: 25–26 December.

☎ **01822 832528.**

🚗 **turn off A390 Tavistock–Liskeard road at Gulworthy Cross 2 miles W of Tavistock, then follow signs.**

📻📻 **£37.50.**

🛏 **£63.**

🛏 **£88.**

In the years since he began cooking here, Peter Gorton has gone from strength to strength, gaining confidence and bravura in his recipes. These draw on many countries but are generally well founded on local produce and seasonality. A confit of rabbit with wild mushrooms and a Madeira sauce is an instance of making something new out of what is shot or gathered on the doorstep; and a sauté of foie gras (not local) on a potato and parsnip pancake, with fresh figs, melds traditions from several cultures into one dish. This is another chef to whom we might turn for leads on creating a modern regional cuisine. The house is handsome: a nineteenth-century residence fit for a mine captain or manager, it has stunning views across the Tamar valley. Loitering with a glass of wine (perhaps Tamar Valley from Harewood Vineyard at Calstock) under the arbour as the sun goes down is an experience worth repeating.

Westcountry dishes: pan-fried medallions of Roborough Park venison and caramelized apples served with black pepper cider sauce; a mille-feuille of Beenleigh Blue and Vulscombe goats' cheese with a beetroot dressing.

HOLNE
FARM B&B
Dodbrooke Farm

Michelcombe, Holne, TQ13 7SP.

Annual closure: one week in October.

☎ **01364 631461.**

🚗 **leaving Holne church on R, turn R then L after 175 m, signed Michelcombe, turn L at foot of hill.**

🍽🍽 £10.

🛏 £17.

🛏 £34.

John and Judy Henderson are members of the Holne Producers' Co-operative which rear and produce venison, Devon black beef, pork and lamb. At Dodbrooke itself they have lamb, duck, and kid and produce their own goats' cheese, yoghourt and milk, cider, free-range eggs, spring water, vegetables and fruits. All this from a farm of 22 acres. It sounds heaven, but try doing it on a cold winter's morning. Judy Henderson claims she's not a Cordon Bleu cook. With materials like that on her doorstep, it's a good thing she isn't, she might be tempted to give them a haute cuisine workout, and so spoil the freshness of it all. Here's a place for a Dartmoor holiday.

HOLNE
B&B
Wellpritton Farm

Holne, TQ13 7RX.

🍽 **19.00.**

☎ **01364 631273.**

🍽🍽 **£9 (unlicensed).**

🛏 **£18.**

🛏 **£36.**

Home cooking by Sue Gifford in an attractive farmhouse complete with goats, horses, rabbits and chickens. Visitors are nicely poised between the twin goals of Dartmoor and the South Hams. Come rain or shine, clotted cream is served every night, but for the remainder, there are substantial meals using local materials.

HORNDON
P
Elephant's Nest Inn

Horndon, PL19 9NQ.

🍽 **11.30–14.00, 18.30–22.00.**

☎ **01822 810273.**

🍽🍽 **£10.**

Once upon a time this was the New Inn, and it is still so named on OS maps. It gained its present name in honour of a very large landlord. It serves as a welcome stopover on moorland hikes, and visitors can rest assured the ducks, goat, rabbits, chickens and geese in the garden have not been made into sandwiches (or casseroles). The blackboard menu will serve as marker to the progress in pub food these last two decades, and in British tastes. Just as curry, not fish and chips, is our favourite food, so this listing hops from Indian lamb to Chinese pork to Texan chilli beef to tandoori chicken. If you want to eat Devonian, try the game pie, some of the fish dishes, or the steak and kidney.

Westcountry dishes: rabbit casserole; Tavy trout; scrumpy pork.

KINGSKERSWELL

P

Barn Owl Inn

Aller Mills, Kingskerswell, TQ12 5AN.

🍴11.30–14.00, 18.30–22.00.

Annual closure: 26 & 27 Dec.

☎ 01803 872130; fax 01803 875279.

🚪 off A380, Newton Abbot to Torquay, signed to the inn.

🍴🍴 £24.95.

🛏 £40.

🛏 £60.

The old farmhouse was grand in its day: elaborate plaster ceiling, panelling and big fireplace in the bar are witness to that. The Warners' restoration, and conversion into a welcoming place to stay, is impressive. Bar food is justifiably popular, and the blackboard is the place to look for daily fish dishes (sole, turbot, hake, squid, scallops and red mullet are mentioned), or for English substantials like apple pie. French chef Denis Lejette holds sway in the restaurant, where menus deliver coulis, melon fans and Earl Grey ice-cream as well as bolder concepts like hake bordelaise with a celeriac purée.

KINGSTEIGNTON

P

Old Rydon Inn

Rydon Road, Kingsteignton, TQ12 3QG.

🍴19.00–21.30 (Mon–Sat, restaurant).

☎ 01626 54626; fax 01626 56980.

🍴🍴 £18.95.

The bar food is as energetic and popular (and cheaper) as that cooked for the restaurant (that only opens in the evenings) at this atmospheric and popular pub that is sometimes so creeper-covered that it's difficult to tell where the walls end and the roof begins. It's in the pub

that you will find venison sausages with bubble and squeak
or a hot pot of venison, pheasant, cured beef and potato, or
lamb with bubble and squeak and crispy parsnips, but the
restaurant may take you on a world tour via dishes like king
prawns on ciabatta, or a Balinese salad of vegetables and
cashews or the Indonesian dish nasi goreng. Perhaps the
most exciting things produced by the kitchen are the substantial meat dishes, like pot-roasted oxtail with cabbage, or
a ragout of hare in a red wine and juniper sauce, or by way
of contrast: the fish. Fresh gurnard in a tempura batter,
skate in black butter or grilled squid with chillies are three
examples.

Westcountry dishes: mussels in cider.

KINGSTON

H

Trebles Cottage Hotel

Kingston, TQ7 4PT.

(🍽) **19.00–20.30.**

☎ **01548 810268.**

🚗 **off A379 Plymouth–Kingsbridge road at Harraton
Cross. Follow signs for Kingston.**

(🍽)(🍽) **£19.50.**

🛏 **£25.**

🛏 **£50.**

The maze of lanes that surround the village may muddle,
but directions will be provided those who 'phone ahead.
Not far from the cottage is Wonwell, one of the best
beaches in south Devon. After a long day of sunshine
(lucky) or vigorous exercise (keeps you dry), Georgie
Kinder's straightforward but well-found cooking ensures
the necessary restoration. A summer dinner that gives
lashings of fresh crab with salad and new potatoes is all one
could want. Follow with bread and butter pudding and
clotted cream and paradise is achieved. That combination of
leeks and pork, met in likky pie, is found here with another
classic Devon item, the dumpling. Salcombe smokies are

smoked mackerel, perhaps served with horseradish, or with gooseberry sauce.

Westcountry dishes: Salcombe smokies; leek and pork casserole with dumplings; chicken in cider.

KNOWSTONE
P
Masons Arms Inn
Knowstone, EX36 4RY.
🍴12.00–14.00, 19.00–21.00.
Annual closure: 25–26 Dec.
☎ 01398 341231/341582.
🍴🍴 £17.80.
🛏 £21.
🛏 £55.

Ploughman's lunches normally come with Westcountry cheeses, though David and Elizabeth Todd have found it impossible to exclude Stilton from Cropwell Bishop in Nottinghamshire. There is also a pie of the day written on the blackboard, alongside curry of the day – a perfect British conjunction. This is a long, thatched pub with a mega-inglenook and some heavy, I mean heavy, beams. The marathon of pies for every day gives a chance for squab pie to get an outing, as well as other winners like their venison, or steak and kidney. These can be eaten in the bar or the restaurant. A nice variation on a theme is their Devonshire cassoulet, using duck, lamb and cider: two regions, one French, one British, each contributing their tithe.

Westcountry dishes: Exmoor venison pie; Devonshire squab pie; Devonshire apple cake.

LEWDOWN
H
Lewtrenchard Manor
Lewdown, EX20 4PN.
🍴12.15–13.45 (Sun), 19.00–21.30 (all week).
☎ 01566 783256/783222; fax 01566 783332.
🚪 just to the S of the old A30, at Lewdown.
🍴🍴 £34.
🛏 £80.
🛏 £105.

The Manor was home to one of the West's great ecclesiastical and literary characters, Sabine Baring Gould (*Onward Christian Soldiers* is his.). The bedrooms and public rooms are heavy with history and memories, but the dining-room (wonderful panelling) offers more modern, country-house fare such as foie gras on a bed of celeriac drizzled with a Madeira sauce. However, there are some interesting variations on British favourites: black pudding served with scallops, pork served with Stilton creamed potatoes and fresh truffle, or roast rabbit with bacon and spring onion pudding and a mustard broth are three examples.

LIFTON
H
Arundell Arms
Fore Street, Lifton, PL16 0AA.
🍴 12.30–14.00, 19.30–21.30.
☎ 01566 784666; fax 01566 784494.
🍴🍴 £21 (lunch), £32 (dinner).
🛏 £64.
🛏 £102.

For years people have been coming to Anne Voss-Bark's hotel to practise their salmon and trout technique. If you are lucky and catch one, perhaps you can have it for dinner. In the winter, off go the fishermen supplanted by the shooters. It's a truly sporting hotel. Not all is blood and guts. Philip Burgess keeps these confined to the kitchen while

producing sophisticated food with technique aplenty, firmly reliant on local producers and the wealth of land and sea. Devon Ruby Red, a beef breed to love and support, is often available, and salmon, of course, is explored in all its variety. Squab pie is another local item – the meat is pork or mutton, not young pigeons as the name might imply.
The cheese board has plenty of local offerings. Bar meals are good: salmon fish cakes recommended.

Westcountry dishes: Devon squab pie; crab and saffron tart with clotted cream.

LOWER ASHTON
P
Manor Inn
Lower Ashton, EX6 7QL.
🍴12.00–13.30, 19.00–21.30 (Tues–Sun).
☎ **01647 252304.**
🍴🍴 **£5.50 (lunch), £12.50 (dinner).**

A tall Scots pine marks the spot. Beneath its crested boughs sits this cheerful pub, with good brews which often as not find their way into steak and ale pie (Teignworthy Bitter) or beef and beer stew. Clare Mann offers fresh home cooking on the menu, with a bar list of sandwiches, ploughman's and jacket potatoes. Character is as varied as much pub cooking nowadays: chillies, lasagne, curries and so forth, but look for today's fish posted on the blackboard, or research Devon fare by means of pies and hearty meat dishes.

Westcountry dishes: Westcountry pie (pork in cider); lamb, leeks and mushrooms in cider.

LYDFORD
H
Castle Inn

Lydford, EX20 4BU.

🍴12.00–14.30, 18.30–21.30 (bar), 19.00–21.30 (restaurant).

Annual closure: Christmas Day.

☎ 01822 820241/2; fax 01822 820454.

🍴🍴 £19.60.

🛏 £30.

🛏 £46.

When King Ethelred was Unready, there was a royal mint at Lydford (also famous as a stannary town – where tin was assayed). The Castle, a hop away from the old castle itself and a short walk from Lydford Gorge, is impressively atmospheric in structure and furnishings. It also has good food (Devon Dining Pub of the Year 1995) with a mixture of the unexpected and the English. A Thai green curry of chicken sits next to pheasant and chestnut casserole (there are Asian curry nights in the winter). Bar food is as good as in the restaurant (which is what the main bar becomes in the evening). Most refreshing of all, they don't do sandwiches but offer instead a Devon cheese platter.

Westcountry dishes: steak and kidney pie with suet crust; scallops in bacon and saffron sauce; parcels of Devon smoked salmon and crab.

LYNTON
H
Alford House Hotel

Alford Terrace, Lynton, EX35 6AT.

🍴 19.00–20.30.

Annual closure: Jan–mid Feb.

☎ 01598 752359.

🍴🍴 £20.

🛏 £22.

🛏 £46.

It's debatable whether the views or the walks make up the bulk of Lynton's charms. Tear yourself away from Countisbury and Foreland Point, and this early Victorian house on the slopes of Sinai, with Brian Peirce's cooking, must come a close second. Dinners play an enterprising variation of local materials. Ostrich steak with a pepper sauce is bound to raise eyebrows, but the invention reflected in combinations such as skate with preserved lemon and cumin, and tayberries with cardamom custard is nicely balanced by the simplicity of grilled sole from the island of Lundy with a parsley butter.

Westcountry dishes: Exmoor trout baked with white wine and herbs; Clovelly skate with preserved lemon and cumin; poached breast of Somerset pheasant with celery and cream.

LYNTON
H
Highcliffe House
Sinai Hill, Lynton, EX35 6AR.
19.00.
☎ 01598 752235.
£34.50.
£45.
£76.

John Bishop and Steven Phillips used to run Hewitt's Hotel, some feet further down the cliffs. Their move to this substantial house, refurbished and decorated to revive its Victorian comforts, has been a great success. Views, once more, are superb. Steven Phillips' cooking has already made its mark. Fresh food, simply presented, include regular outings for his Gordon's Gin tomato soup, and some good ways with Exmoor venison, be it as terrine or pie or a ragout with stout, port, pickled walnuts and wild mushrooms.

Westcountry dishes: venison pie.

MORCHARD BISHOP
FARMHOUSE B&B
Wigham

Morchard Bishop, EX17 6RJ.

🍴19.30.

☎ 01363 877350.

🚌 **1.5 miles NW of Morchard Bishop, off road to Chulmleigh.**

🍴🍴 £24.

🛏 £46.

🍳 £70.

Wigham is a large thatched farmhouse heavy with age. The Chilcotts seem able to run it as a busy guest house while still coping with the farm alongside. Dawn Chilcott did admit that they do not grow quite so many vegetables as they used to, 'as there are never enough hours in the day.' Even so, beef, lamb, pork, sausages, bacon, eggs, butter, milk and cream all come from the farm, and they make their own bread. Everyone sits down to one long table for dinner – it gives a chance to get acquainted – and Dawn Chilcott does not offer a choice, although guests have a chance to voice likes and dislikes. The cooking has plenty of undertones of Devon, even if many dishes are not themselves certified 'ancient and traditional'. When so close to the source, all cooking is regional, whether the ideas are new or old.

Westcountry dishes: mackerel with gooseberry sauce; beef stew and dumplings; celery and pork in cider; bramble soufflé.

MORTEHOE
<u>H</u>
Watersmeet Hotel
Mortehoe, EX34 7EB.
🍴12.30–14.00, 19.00–20.30.
Annual closure: Dec–Jan.
☎ 01271 870333; fax 01271 870890.
🍴🍴 £25.
🛏 £57.
🛏 £85.

Watersmeet means what it says: the hotel is a spit away from the beach, large windows giving that inside-outside feeling. Cookery steers a nice course between elaboration, which gets exhausting day after day for holiday residents, and simplicity, which gets boring. Good meats and fish, Westcountry cheeses, and the occasional British pudding.

Westcountry dishes: medallions of Devon beef with Exmoor ale.

MORETONHAMPSTEAD
<u>C</u>
Gateway Tea Room
17 The Square, Moretonhampstead.
🍴10.30–18.00 all week (summer); Weds–Mon (Sept–Dec); weekends (Jan–Easter).
☎ 01647 440722; fax 01647 440100.
🍴🍴 £5.00.

The secret of this small café run by Jane Wimberley lies at Great Howton Farm a mile away, where Alastair Wimberley tends the suckler herd, the sheep and the poultry and the acres are devoted to supplying the larder. Farmhouse cooking means cakes and pasties, and the future holds opportunities of bed and breakfast and evening meals at the farm as well.

Westcountry dishes: Devonshire pasties.

NORTH BOVEY

H
Blackaller

North Bovey, TQ13 8QY.

(🍴)20.00, Tues–Sun.

Annual closure: Jan–Feb.

☎ 01647 440322.

🚪 on the road to North Bovey out of Moretonhampstead.

(🍴)(🍴) £27.

🛏 £29.

🛎 £34.

This former woollen mill on the banks of a river, with beehives producing honey for breakfast and a flock of Jacob's sheep for lamb and wool is monument to the beauties of Devon. The flagstoned longhouse has comfortable bedrooms and a lived-in feel to the public rooms. Peter Hunt is a gentle host and Hazel Phillips takes charge of the cooking. The kitchen rarely takes in 'foreign' food: 'All my dishes use only local ingredients,' writes Hazel. 'Venison, salmon, trout, cheese (all from the Westcountry), wild mushrooms gathered on our own land,' she continues, ending with a rousing list of vegetables and soft fruit grown in their garden. It sounds like 'The Good Life', but long hours are needed to support it. If most materials are local, cookery is intelligent simplicity with a dose of enlivening spice: prawn soufflé on a bed of ginger mushrooms; monkfish on tagliatelle with a prawn curry and coriander sauce; barbary duck marinated in Blackaller honey; syrup and lemon tart are some instances. Sharpham and Whitestone wines are on the list, to round off a gastronomic tour of the West.

Westcountry dishes: apple cider pork; plum soufflé with Dittisham plums; apple and cider cake.

NORTHLEIGH
FARMHOUSE B&B
Smallicombe Farm

Northleigh, EX13 6BU.
Annual closure: Christmas Day.
☎ **01404 831310; fax 01404 831431.**
🍴🍴 **£9.50.**
🛏 **£18.50.**
🛏 **£37.00.**

Ian Todd cooks the breakfast, Maggie Todd the dinner,
though how either of them have the time between running
their rare-breeds farm is a mystery. Berkshire, British Lop
and Middle White pigs are reared, for pork, ham, sausages
and bacon. Dorset Down sheep deliver the lamb. Devon
and Dexter cows take care of the beef. Eggs are free-range
from the barnyard. Ian Todd's fried bread gets many mentions in the visitors' book; even his wife will admit that. Her
evening meals, however, show the range of possibilities for
this cornucopia of produce. Her mention of bullaces (an
early variety of plum, one step up from sloe) is reminder of
the importance of the orchard in so many Westcountry
farms. Not all varieties are grown on modern dwarf root-
stock but may have stood for decades, if not longer.

Westcountry dishes: leg of pork with cider, cream and
apples; shoulder of pork casseroled with cider and seasonal
vegetables; bullace crumble.

OAKFORD
FARMHOUSE B&B
Harton Farm

Oakford, EX16 9HH.
🍴 **19.30.**
Annual closure: Christmas, New Year, and lambing.
☎ **01398 351209.**
🚗 **at end of lane off B3227.**
🍴🍴 **£10 (residents only).**
🛏 **£13.**
🛏 **£26.**

Come lambing-time, the Heads put ewes before guests: the constant attention required by a flock of expectant sheep is greater than the most demanding human. For the rest of the year, their farm revolves around the kitchen. They chose their stock breeds with an eye to flavour: Aberdeen Angus cross cattle, Gloucester Old Spot pigs, Exmoor Horn crossed with Oxford Down sheep. Lindy Horn manages the garden to produce year-round vegetables, in meals that march with the seasons, not against them. So, no air-freighted snow peas, but a patch of eleven different sorts of cabbage (brassica) to give greenstuff in every month. In summer and autumn she's into the hedgerows to gather rosehips for syrup, rowanberries and crab apples for jelly, soft fruits, and elderflower for cordial for thirsty haymakers. In miniature, this is the Westcountry larder, and it makes no odds whether Lindy's recipes are time-honoured local instructions handed from aunt to niece and on to the next generation, the food is local.

OAKFORD
FARMHOUSE B&B
Newhouse Farm

Oakford, EX16 9JE.

🍴 19.00.

Annual closure: Christmas, first three weeks of March (lambing).

☎ 01398 351347.

🚪 **5 miles W of Bampton on B3227 (do not go into Oakford village).**

🍴🍴 £11.

🛏 £20.

🍽 £38.

Anne Boldry is something of a crusader for Devon cooking and proper food. She laments that some visitors bridle at the thought of £11 for dinner and go to the pub 'for something cheaper' – frozen chicken Kiev, microwaved lasagne and so on. But at Newhouse, complete with its own old bread oven and stock and produce enough to feed a hundred families, she will put 'high dumpsie dearie' jam on your breakfast table (along with maybe up to thirteen other home-made preserves that she has in her larder). That 'high dumpsie deary', Mrs Boldry says, came from a Somerset recipe. 'Dumpsie' or 'dimpsy' is Devonshire dialect for dusk or dark, which describes the jam accurately enough. It is an orchard fruit mixture made dark by plums. It should also have, she says, some pears in it, and maybe this accounts for the 'dearie' part of the name. Her explanation is, 'You just dumps it in m'deary.' The Irish have a similar jam called 'mixty maxty'. Enough of jams: the farm produces vegetables, beef and lamb into the bargain. Anne Boldry's in and out pudding is made with apples and almonds, like an Eve's pudding; her squab pie is pork and apple; and her clotted cream is farmhouse. The proud face of British cookery.

Westcountry dishes: squab pie; lamb stew; in and out pudding; venison cooked in elderberry wine.

PARKHAM
B&B
Old Rectory

Rectory Lane, Parkham, EX39 5PL.
🍴19.45.
Annual closure: Nov–Feb.
☎ 01237 451443.
🍴🍴 £27.
🛏 £50.
🛌 £72.

An advantage of an old rectory is that the visitor can use the church tower as navigational aid. Guided by such a beacon, aim for this restful house with walled garden and some excellent cooking by Jean Langton. Her inspiration may well be French – dishes such as tarte tatin, or pork à la Normande appear on her menus – but the supplies are eminently Devon, from the beef and pork from her own village, to the Gloucester Old Spot pork taken from Ann Petch at Heal Farm, or the fruit and vegetables grown for her by dedicated neighbours.

Westcountry dishes: Tamar salmon with herby sauce; cider syllabub.

PARRACOMBE
H
Heddon's Gate

Heddon's Mouth, Parracombe, EX31 4PZ.
🍴20.00.
Annual closure: Nov–Mar.
☎ 01598 763313; fax 01598 763363.
🚗 turn off A39, 4 miles W of Lynton, signed to Martinhoe, then the road signed to Heddon's Mouth.
🍴🍴 £28.
🛏 £26.
🛌 £48.

This former hunting lodge is hemmed in by the woods of the Heddon valley, and the ravishing views soar over tree tops to the slopes beyond. Every day, Robert Deville lays out a cream tea for his happy residents – all part of the package: lucky them. As evening draws in, they may sit to a five-course meal with a choice of two main courses and more than that at pudding. The cooking develops out of the location: chicken is roasted and served with tarragon sauce and laverbread croquettes; the beef is often Red Devon; the sausages are made locally, as are the chocolates nibbled with after-dinner coffee (from the estimable Melchior Chocolates of South Molton). New potatoes from Combe Martin (particularly early) are welcome arrivals, and soft fruit abounds in the months which follow, succeeded by wild mushrooms gathered on the doorstep. Cookery of seasonality, lavish, and generous. For apple dappy, see the entry for Hurdon Farm, Launceston, Cornwall.

Westcountry dishes: Devonshire junket; apple dappy; Devonshire cream tea.

PLYMOUTH
<u>R</u>
Chez Nous
13 Frankfort Gate, Plymouth, PL1 1QA.
🍴12.30–14.00, 19.00–22.30 Tues–Sat.
Annual closure: Feb & Sept.
☎ **01752 266793.**
🍴🍴 £32.

Since 1974 Jacques Marchal has been a fixture in Frankfort Gate, every bit as French today as when he donned a Maurice Chevalier panama and a blue-striped apron. Suzanne, his wife, is not French herself but Plymouth born and bred. Inside Chez Nous you may think yourself transported to the Vosges, Jacques' homeland. Music, flags, pictures, all the accoutrements of a bistrot français, and the menu written on a blackboard continues the illusion. It needs translation by Suzanne, and is French in method and inspiration. 'What's this doing in a guide to Westcountry

Cooking?' you ask. The answer is that in the late '70s, Jacques Marchal's was one of the few restaurants in the region where the customer could guarantee to find local produce, spankingly fresh, treated with sympathy. This still holds good. St Enedoc asparagus from Cornwall, fish from the Barbican in Plymouth, baby vegetables from the Tamar Valley, milk, cream and butter from Langage Farm at Plympton: these are the notes which Jacques composes into a marvellous tune, with dishes such as duck with lentils, spinach ravioli, monkfish with saffron, or venison with port.

SALCOMBE
H
Soar Mill Cove Hotel
Salcombe, TQ7 3DS.
🍴 **12.00–14.00, 19.15–21.00.**
Annual closure: 3 Jan–6 Feb.
☎ **01548 561566; fax 01548 561223.**
🚗 **from A381 at Marlborough, follow signs after church.**
🍴🍴 **£26.**
🛏 **£72.**
🛏 **£104.**

The sandy cove that gives its name to the hotel is pretty impressive: we have got used to thinking of sea and sand as the preserve of tropical islands. Those more interested in their appetites will soon turn to the long menu that Keith Makepeace has developed in his years as proprietor. It repays study. A gloss of haute cuisine does not disguise the strong roots in the locality. A whole roasted Hardwick lamb is carved to order and served with tayberry tartlets, mint jelly and strong gravy; scallops from Salcombe are rolled in a Provençal tapénade mixture and served with fresh crab-meat; new-wave pasties are filled with a surf and turf of beef and crab; Curworthy cheese is baked in a tart and finished with foaming Devon nut-brown butter. Then there are the more traditional recipes, of which Exeter pudding is a fine example. The original calls for a tin to be lined with ratafia biscuits and raisins, filled with an egg, lemon, bread-crumb and suet mixture, layered with jam before baking.

Westcountry dishes: Soar Bay crab cakes; Devonshire junket; Exeter pudding; Cornish yarg soufflé.

STAVERTON
H
Kingston Estate

Kingston House, Staverton, TQ9 6AR.
🍴 20.00.
Annual closure: Christmas/New Year.
☎ 01803 762235; fax 01803 762444.
🚌 at Staverton, take left fork at Sea Trout Inn sign-posted Kingston..
🍴🍴 £30.75.
🛏 £65.
🛏 £100.

Devon's country houses are often guarded secrets, hidden in valleys rarely in the public eye. Kingston is magnificent, large, classical, and little known. The Corfield family have rescued it from oblivion, and we can visit, sleep, dine, stay in one of the cottages and generally enjoy either the rich history of the interiors (at least one 1830s bathroom), parade up and down the marquetry staircase, or wander the parterres so cleverly fashioned where lately there was naught. It is in keeping with some of that revivalism that Piers Corfield cooks chicken to eighteenth- or seventeenth-century recipes and grows old and vanishing varieties of vegetables, herbs and roses in his garden. Reservations need to be a day or two in advance for the dining-room, and the meal will be longer or shorter depending on numbers, but be sure it will have some nice historical reference and be composed according to season. Cheeses are from Ticklemore Cheese Shop in Totnes. Riverford Farm, with its organic produce, is in the same parish.

Westcountry dishes: home–made pasties; Devon fish pie; Devonshire drops.

STOKE CANON
H
Barton Cross

Huxham, Stoke Canon, EX5 4EJ.

🍴19.00–21.30, Mon–Sat.

☎ 01392 841245; fax 01392 841942.

🚌 at Stoke Canon on A396 Exeter to Tiverton road, turn right (E) at church.

🍴🍴 £30.

🛏 £63.50.

🛏 £78.50.

Thatch to the right, tiles to the left, greet arrivals to this cottage, now expanded and elevated to hotel. Inside, massive beams proclaim ancient origins, especially in the galleried dining-room that soars to the apex of the cruck. Elsewhere, bedrooms are resolutely mod. con. Paul George Bending is a chef who cures his own beef for bresaola and pairs it with confit of duck to create the 'Huxham winter platter' appearing on one of his seasonal menus. Come summer, vegetables are home-grown, and potted salmon and crab is worth trying. While the modus operandi leans more to professionalism than robust home cookery, the kitchen appreciates what may be gathered in the hedgerows or bought from farm shops, as well as merely aping big-city fashion.

Westcountry dishes: leg of lamb steak with bubble and squeak and an onion gravy; fish soup with saffron; local game; bread, butter and bramley pudding.

STRETE
R
Laughing Monk

Totnes Road, Strete, TQ6 0RN.

🍴19.00–21.30 (Tues–Sat), 12.00–14.00 (last Sun of month only).

☎ 01803 770639.

🍴🍴 £23.

There is not a lot that is monkish about this cheerful restaurant in a converted village school down the coast from Dartmouth. Within the time it takes to say the paternoster the Rothwells deliver very decent food that turns modern variations on what's available from the weekly marketing.

Westcountry dishes: mussels from the Avon cooked in shells with shallots, garlic, parsley, white wine and cream; savoury apple.

TIVERTON
FARMHOUSE B&B
Lower Collipriest Farm
Tiverton, EX16 4PT.
🍴**Mar–Oct.**
Annual closure: Nov–Feb.
☎ **01884 252321.**
🍴🍴 **£12.**
🛏 **£20.**
🛏 **£40.**

The farmhouse is impressively thatched, in the midst of a couple of hundred acres, with ponds and woodlands as extras. Linda Olive keeps in touch with her location, baking her own bread, serving her own marmalade or honey from close by, and relying on Tiverton market for much of her supplies. Her excellent dinners have many Devon overtones. How rarely is junket found on restaurant menus, yet here is a dish that has always been associated with Devon and Cornwall? A Victorian traveller once wrote that, 'nothing good has come out of Cornwall except junket and the *Cornwall Examiner*.' Junket is so called because the cream was drained in a basket, named joncade in old French. In fact, there is not a lot to connect it to Devonshire or Cornwall beyond popular association, and there are many similar curds and whey dishes in the rest of England.

Westcountry dishes: junket with clotted cream; pork with prunes, sage and cider; pears poached in cider.

TORQUAY
R(WITH ROOMS)
Mulberry House
1 Scarborough Road, Torquay, TQ2 5UJ.
🍴**12.00–14.00, 19.30–21.30 (Weds–Sat & Sun lunch).**
Annual closure: first two weeks Jan.
☎ **01803 213639.**
🍴🍴 **£18.50.**
🛏 **£25.**
🛏 **£45.**

Lesley Cooper has created one of Torquay's most distinctive restaurants and places to stay. It began life ten years ago as a mainly daytime café (but it was always pretty special) and has gradually developed where Lesley's energies have taken her. There is nothing more appetizing than the array of sweet dishes and cakes that greet the visitor on entry. They are almost enough to make you want to eat a back-to-front meal. That would be unfair to the rest of it. I sometimes think the food might be best likened to superhuman home cooking. It always tastes as if it was done just for you, and was bought for you too.

Westcountry dishes: pheasant with apple, cream and cider; crab and Cheddar tart with mixed salad leaves; Devon apple cake with butterscotch cream sauce; grilled lobster with dill butter sauce

TORQUAY
H
Osborne Hotel
Hesketh Crescent, Torquay, TQ1 2LL.
🍴**brasserie 12.00–14.30, 18.00–21.30 (all day in summer); restaurant 19.00–21.30.**
☎ **01803 213311; fax 01803 296788.**
🍴🍴 **£16.50 (brasserie), £22.50 (restaurant).**
🛏 **£41.**
🛏 **£103.**

The hotel occupies a grand nineteenth-century crescent, built when Torquay entered the stakes of fashionable watering-hole for the English holidaymaker, long before the advent of Eurostar. Cooking, whether in the brasserie or the more serious restaurant, is in the vein of grand hotels everywhere, but there are still some regional jewels to pull from their international setting, and mention should be made of the good fish supplies which the kitchens enjoy – as perhaps they should, given their location.

Westcountry dishes: Brixham crab soufflé; Torbay sole with mussels stew; baked apples in cinnamon custard; roasted loin of pork with crispy crackling in cider sauce.

TORQUAY
<u>R</u>
Table
135 Babbacombe Road, Torquay, TQ1 3SR.
12.15–1.45, 19.15–21.45.
Annual closure: 2 weeks Feb, 2 weeks Mar.
☎ **01803 324292.**
£14.50 (lunch), £31.50 (dinner).

Julie Tuckett's front-room restaurant keeps its menus short so that produce may be as fresh and immediate as possible. She does not indulge in too many culinary fireworks, allowing prime quality to show for itself, particularly with the fish bought daily from Brixham. Her fish soup, rusty, deep and odorous, is an excellent distillation. It's strange how a tradition of fish soup has never caught on in Britain, and our models are French, Italian, American or Asian. A speciality pudding that has nothing to do with Devon, but everything with pleasure, is her apricot brioche soufflé.

TRUSHAM
P (WITH ROOMS)
Cridford Inn

Trusham, TQ13 0NR.

🍴 12.15–13.45, 18.45–20.45.

Annual closure: Christmas Day.

☎ 01626 853694.

🍴🍴 £23.00.

🛏 £40.

🛏 £60.

Ecstatic London journalists have described David Hesmondhalgh's ploughman's lunch: not just a lump of supermarket Cheddar, but a plate of four or five sorts, including Ticklemore Goat, Beenleigh Blue, Sharpham and Cornish Yarg to keep local flags aflutter. Sausages and mash? Organically-reared wild boar, venison or pork, with a fistful of flavourings, from Riverford Farm near Totnes. His home-smoker deals with salmon, chicken and cheese, and fish from Brixham is fuel for his pies, which are served with tapénade, a condiment made from olives, capers and tuna (not Devon, this, but Provençal). Join these local extravaganzas to a sound and ably-cooked menu in both restaurant and bars and you have a model of pub grub. The Inn was rescued and restored by the Hesmondhalghs, they replaced a tin roof with thatch, but in origin it is perhaps the oldest domestic building in Devon (that's what they're saying, anyway), with a mention in Domesday Book, displaying a late-medieval window in the bar, and getting a credit in Pevsner's *Buildings of Devon* as a medieval hall house with Tudor or Jacobean floors inserted to give the early owners more rooms.

Westcountry dishes: Devonshire fish pie.

TWO BRIDGES
H
Cherrybrook Hotel
Two Bridges, PL20 6SP.
🍴 **19.00–19.30.**
Annual closure: Christmas.
☎ **01822 880260.**
🚌 **1 mile from Two Bridges cross, on B3212.**
🍴🍴 **£20.**
🛏 **£26.**
🛏 **£52.**

Cherrybrook was once a farmhouse. It sounds like a children's summer hideaway – *The Famous Five go to Cherrybrook Farm*, perhaps. A glance at the list of the Duncans' suppliers shows that local farmers are still very much part of the recipe. Anne Monro for lamb, pork and veal; Richard Vines for beef; Stuart Baker for lamb and pork; Yard Farm for ice cream; and Toatley Farm for yoghourt. Ann Duncan's cooking, too, turns what comes to hand into food with a noticeable goût de terroir: twice-baked Vulscombe goats' cheese soufflé; the Tamar Valley soup made of cauliflower and broccoli – vegetables that benefit from the soft climate of the region to make an early appearance in metropolitan markets; cider-baked mackerel; or vanilla clotted-cream ice-cream splashed with Capton Vineyard raspberry or strawberry liqueur. Cheese, it goes without saying, is usually from Devon. The view across the high moor is remarkable – although it may be less enticing as banks of mist settle on snow – and there is enough home ground to provide fresh air and lungs to the house (as well as the odd goat).

Westcountry dishes: Devonshire Porker (pork chop, cider, onions and apple); Tamar valley soup; broccoli and Devon Blue soup; Devon apple cake.

UGBOROUGH
FARMHOUSE B&B
Hillhead Farm
Ugborough, PL21 0HQ.

🍴19.00 (residents only).

Annual closure: Christmas.

☎ 01752 892674; fax 01752 690111.

🚐 half a mile up the Bittaford/Ivybridge road from Ugborough, on RHS.

🍴🍴 £10 (unlicensed).

🛏 £18.

🛏 £36.

The farmhouse is slate-hung on most sides: it was the best way to stop the driving rain penetrating the thick stone walls. Outside the gate, the dog lazes against the mounting block. A background rumble of machinery is sign of ongoing labour. Farm B&Bs give a flavour of real life. The Johns' farm supplies the lamb for evening meals, and the garden does the mint. Home production, as in so many other farmhouses where guests are made welcome, is the essence of it all. Jane Johns remarks on her rhubarb and gooseberries: harvest them, and turn them into fools, or crumbles, or pie. Flavour them with angelica or elderflower; serve them with thick clotted cream. From a single fruit, so many dishes may result – thus the cook never tires of a particular ingredient when it seems to come in glut.

Westcountry dishes: Cornish pasties; junket.

VIRGINSTOW
R (WITH ROOMS)
Percy's at Coombeshead
Virginstow, EX21 5EA.

🍴12.00, 19.00.

☎ 01409 211236; fax 01409 211275.

🍴🍴 £25.

🛏 £34.

🛏 £68.

Much as converts are often the most eloquent spokesmen, so the Bricknell-Webbs have come to Devon and are preaching the gospel of Westcountry food. They have another restaurant in north London and supply it with vegetables and greenstuffs from their new garden at Virginstow. The restaurant itself is in the old longhouse, while bedrooms are in converted barns across the yard. Tina Bricknell-Webb is in charge of all the cooking and the largely local sourcing of the ingredients, much home-grown. The cookery itself is of that creative modern British eclecticism, rather than researching byways of culinary history. But to be named 'Local Produce Champions' of 1997 by one national guide is an achievement in your first year. Some encouraging words from Tina herself are to be found elsewhere in this volume.

WEST BUCKLAND
FARMHOUSE B&B
Huxtable Farm
West Buckland, EX32 0SR.
🍴19.30–21.00.
Annual closure: 20–28 Dec.
☎ 01598 760254.
🍴🍴 £13.
🛏 £25.
🛏 £44.

Here you may take four-course candle-lit dinners in a medieval longhouse. There's an eighty-acre sheep farm. Suffolk-cross sheep are the mainstay, but there are Jacobs ewes for lamb for the table. Until a few years ago, the Paynes kept three Jersey house-cows, making clotted cream, cottage cheese and yoghourt, and feeding the pigs with the skimmed milk. Unfortunately, new regulations have made such an enterprise unrealistic. Even so, consider Jackie's reaction to the passing seasons: 'sloes, elderberries, crab apples, hazelnuts, and wild mushrooms in the autumn, elderflowers, nettles and wild strawberries in the first days of summer,' all to be gathered and cooked with. If that is not enough, read the book: *Huxtable, the story of a*

Devon farm. This sounds close to paradise, and for those in search of Westcountry cookery as well as ingredients, Jackie has raided enough books and memories to offer an unparalleled series. Apple in and apple out cake is a steamed suet pudding. Devon beef stew may be related to Exeter stew, also served with parsley dumplings. Dumplings were a common accompaniment to such dishes. In south Devon they were called nackerjacks, in the north, naggerjacks. 'Devonshire stew', however, was not a meat stew but made entirely from vegetables – mainly cabbage and potatoes. Whortleberry cream fudge is a monument to two strands of locality: the fudge that now floods the tourist shops and tables of the South West (a by-product of cream), and the wealth of the summer hedgerows in the woods on the moorland edge.

Westcountry dishes: apple in and apple out cake; Devon beef stew with parsley dumplings; whortleberry cream fudge.

WIDECOMBE IN THE MOOR
<u>P</u>

Ragglestone Inn
Widecombe in the Moor, TQ13 7TF.
🍴12.00–14.00, 19.00–21.00.
☎ 01364 621327; fax 01364 621224.
🍴🍴 £13.

Take the lane to Venton out of the village centre, it's signposted to this small and unspoilt inn where Devon cookery is still practised, blessed by the absence of curry and lasagne. Instead, eat pies, pasties, Devon cheese for a ploughman's, blackberry and apple pie (with clotted cream) and many other substantial and properly cooked meals. There should be more like this.

Westcountry dishes: rabbit pie; squab pie; pasties; Devon apple sausage casserole

WILMINGTON
<u>H</u>
Home Farm
Wilmington, EX14 9JR.
🍴12.00–14.15, 19.00–21.30.
Annual closure: 25–26 Dec.
☎ 01404 831278; fax 01404 831411.
🍴🍴 £18.
🛏 £32.
🛏 £60.

Gone are the cows in the byre, the horses in the stable, and
all the farm buildings as well as the Tudor thatched farmhouse have been converted to the comings and goings of
hotel guests in this handsome place on the edge of the
village of Wilmington. There is much clean stone and
heavy beams to impart atmosphere and Barry Bingham
labours manfully in the kitchen producing a daily menu
and a longer, less frequently changing, à la carte. Expect
to find Denhay air-dried ham, vegetables from Miller's
Farm Shop in Axminster, smoked fish from the Dartmouth
Smokehouse and other local produce, but the style of the
cookery is more mainstream than consciously south-
western.

WINKLEIGH

<u>R</u>

Pophams

Castle Street, Winkleigh, EX19 8HU.

🍴11.45-15.00 (Tues-Sat).

Annual closure: Feb.

☎ 01837 83767.

🍴🍴 £22 (unlicensed).

When Ralph Schumacher wrote his economic classic *Small is Beautiful*, he must have been thinking of Pophams. It's so small, a fat man would have trouble turning round. The problem is, the food's so good, many people turn to fat just thinking about it. The food is cooked on one side of the counter, the world tucks in on the other. All the time there is running commentary from Dennis Hawkes, who acts the host, and Melvyn Popham, who cooks. It may be tiny, but the cooking has no self-imposed restrictions, and the style can be remarkably assured as well as direct. Great pies, excellent salmon with a hollandaise, best end of lamb in puff pastry with Madeira sauce to die for. This is a Devon experience that all should savour.

Westcountry dishes: **pork chops in local Inch's cider with sage and apples.**

Dorset

Introduction

'Before starting we'll one and all come to my house and have a rasher of bacon; then every man-jack get a pint of cider into his inside; then we'll warm up an extra drop wi' some mead and a bit of ginger; everyone take a thimbleful... to finish off his inner man – Why sonnies a man's not himself till he is fortified wi' a bit and a drop.'

Thomas Hardy, *Under the Greenwood Tree.*

Village names, Piddletrenthide, Winterborne Tomson, Purse Caundle, Owermoigne, have reverberations of country life, summer evenings and dawn choruses that set city-dwellers' hearts a-quiver. The villages themselves, churches, manor houses, even mansions, combine to swell the chord. Dorset has barely been invaded by the tentacles of megalopolis; even the shadow of Bournemouth is mitigated by a cordon of heathland. On the way to nowhere, motorway and railway have passed it by, leaving one of the most steadfastly rural areas in the country.

Unlike many southern counties, Dorset has always been agricultural. No medieval industrial heritage, left in ruins after the shift northwards in the coal age. The towns are market towns, never pretending to much more than they now achieve. Lyme Regis and Poole have always had some significance in coastal trade, but Poole was the more important in terms of world-wide commerce. Newfoundland was the foundation of her prosperity – far greater, at the start, than Bournemouth's; the latter, with Weymouth, only coming to prominence, existence indeed, with the fashion for sea bathing.

In step with its neighbours, Dorset is primarily a live-stock producer. The traditions of cheese and cream encountered there are found here. It is not simple replication: here, after all, can be found blue vinney, a particular and unique cheese, as well as Dorset blue (full fat where blue vinney is made from whey after cream and butter have been taken).

Few lambs are better than those from Dorset. There is a small breed, now uncommon, called Portland, that produces a particularly succulent and full-flavoured meat. In common with many of the smaller, older strains, this sheep has a more catholic diet than the modern hybrid. Its appetite for weeds, pickings from the hedgerows and more robust plants than grass giving it a more intense, stronger, flavour.

Perhaps proximity to Wiltshire has made pig breeding an important element of the agricultural scene. The pig gave Wiltshire a reputation for lardy cake and it has travelled through Dorset to the coast. The Portland lardy is held in high esteem and many bakers claim to cook it to a traditional recipe, whether in Portland or no. A variant is dripping cake, also of Westcountry origin. It must have been developed for beef farmers.

A delicacy claimed by one district as peculiar to itself will surface in another. Often, one is witnessing the patchy survival of a dish once cooked throughout the nation. At other times, the recipe may have a regional validity, but the region itself has been lost to the more parochial boundaries of towns or counties. Thus apple cake, an apple tart cooked first with its pastry on top, then reversed to the bottom so that the apples may be sugared and creamed before being eaten. This is described as a speciality of Cornwall; can be found on café blackboards in Devon advertised as 'Devon Apple Cake'; and is deemed by Dorset to be its especial skill. A more common Dorset variation is made as a risen cake, not as pastry, thus allowing Devon and Cornwall their particular affection for pastry and pies.

The Dorset knob is an example of instant tradition. These thrice-cooked biscuits were celebrated by Thomas Hardy, who invested much that he wrote with the patina of time. But Dorset cobs were the invention of one man not much more than a century ago – his family still makes them today.

It is intriguing to speculate why the specialities of counties such as Dorset, Devon and Cornwall should revolve around pastry and bread. They were not primarily wheat growing districts. Here were two balmy climes that could grow garden crops that never would thrive in less hospitable places. (According to the garden writer and diarist John Evelyn in the seventeenth century, Dorset was allegedly the first place in England to grow the large cabbage; Devon could boast broccoli and cauliflower; Cornwall saffron and early crops.) Flour could be got anywhere. Even if a district had a reputation for certain crops, it did not necessarily follow that expertise in devising recipes to use them would be confined to the region of production.

Although Dorset has few dishes to its name, it partakes of a regional identity common to its neighbours in the South West: cider, cream, fish, sheep. And in recent years, it has nursed several important small producers, for instance of pork and ham, cheese and dairy products, crayfish and watercress, in the bosom of its generous agriculture.

Some local dishes:

Dorset sausage
Jugged steak
Ham flan
Pickled pork
Dorset knobs
Dorset apple cake
Apple dumplings
Blackmore Vale cake

BEAMINSTER
<u>H</u>

Bridge House Hotel

Beaminster, DT8 3AY.

🍴12.30–14.00, 19.00–21.00.

☎ 01308 862200; fax 01308 863700.

🍴🍴 £19.50 (lunch), £25.95 (dinner).

🛏 £55.

🛏 £62.

Deep in Hardy country, Peter Pinkster's hotel presents an impressive medieval front to the street – it was originally a priest's house. In the secluded garden, a conservatory is locale for lunch. Come evening, food and its service migrates to a handsome dining-room that manages to combine memories of that priestly occupation with an elegance more in tune with Jane Austen. Peter Pinkster remarked that when, not so long ago, they cooked Dorset dishes during Thomas Hardy Week, they had little support for their efforts. His menus, therefore, run along more familiar 'modern' lines of gnocchi, king prawns, pork with apricot and cashews, or duck with ginger, lime and honey. England's magpie tendency to gather to its taste-buds flavours and techniques of other nations, at the expense of earlier native preferences, is well illustrated, and no doubt justified. However, Westcountry Cooking may change that, may give zest to a return to English inspiration, while keeping the best of contemporary eclecticism.

Westcountry dishes: Denhay ham.

CHEDINGTON

H
Chedington Court
Chedington, DT8 3HY.
🍴 19.00–20.45.
Annual closure: January.
☎ 01935 891265; fax 01935 891442.
🍴🍴 £32.50.
🛏 £62.
🛎 £104.

New owners Anne and John Roberts succeed the Chapmans who ruled here for more than twenty years. The relaxed yet comfortable tone of the place continues, and the kitchen remains under the care of Lindsay Wakeman. The Court is a Victorian house in the Jacobean style – quarry-loads of honeyed stone – overlooking enviable garden and parkland towards a golf course (once part and parcel of the hotel) a mile distant. The cookery draws upon that country-house currency familiar in Britain today. Curried parsnip soup, which sometimes appears on the menus, could act as a litmus test (another is carrot and coriander soup). The invention of the cookery writer Jane Grigson in the '70s, it catches the imagination of many country-house kitchens. A familiar (and inexpensive) ingredient, a desirable silky texture, and a touch of the exotic from the curry spices. It seems inextricably British, yet was created only yesterday. No criticism, just an aside on the birth of tradition. Country-house means a level of sophistication, also reflected in dishes like loin of lamb with mushrooms and spinach wrapped in thin pastry, or chicken roasted with cumin, coriander and cardamom, served with a herb and cream sauce. Suppliers are good. Phil Bowditch brings fish from Taunton, as does Mr Park from MFV *October Morning* in West Bay, Bridport; cheese and bacon are brought over from Denhay Farm (and only Westcountry cheeses are offered in the dining-room), and Loders in Crewkerne supply the meat.

CORSCOMBE
P

Fox Inn

Corscombe, DT2 0NJ.

🍴 12.00–14.00, 19.00–21.00 (21.30 Fri–Sat).

Annual closure: 25 Dec.

☎ 01935 891330.

🚍 **on the Halstock road.**

🍴🍴£17.

The Fox is another of those ludicrously pretty pubs: all whitewash and thatch, with tables dotted through the succession of spaces and bars – anywhere that can take the crowds that throng, in fact, including across the lane by the stream on sunny days. Will Longman, who cooks, has a strong local following from his years in Bridport. The menu, which changes from day to day, is very strong on fish (mullet, scallops, clams, shellfish, seabass, etc.); excellent for rabbit pie, or rabbit braised with rosemary and cream; estimable for venison with red wine; and spare a thought for the puddings such as caramelized apple pie, plum crumble, or home-made ices. There's even home-produced elderflower cordial. Sometimes pubs are all eye and no substance: not the Fox.

Westcountry dishes: Abbotsbury oysters ; Westcountry fish pie; meringues with clotted cream.

DORCHESTER
R

Mock Turtle

34 High West Street, Dorchester, DT1 1UP.

🍴12.00–14.00 (Tues–Fri); 19.00–21.30 (Mon–Sat).

Annual closure: 25–26 Dec, 1 Jan.

☎ 01305 264011.

🍴🍴 £21.50 (lunch); £28.75 (dinner).

An elegant bow front attracts passers-by to the Mock Turtle, though the soup of that name is not on the menu.

What you find is attractive treatment of plenty of fish, Dorset lamb and other meats in a lively Medi-Pacific style (i.e. lots of spices and risottos and things). But there is also a trio of lamb cutlets with bubble and squeak, or Dorset blue vinney cheese used as a stuffing for mushrooms or as a base for a celery soup, or Denhay ham served with tabbouleh (a Middle Eastern cracked-wheat salad). This mix and match makes for cheerful eating.

Westcountry dishes: Portland crab pancakes.

LOWER BOCKHAMPTON
H

Yalbury Cottage

Lower Bockhampton, DT2 8PZ.

🍴19.00–21.00; 15.00–17.30 for teas in summer season. Annual closure: Jan.

☎ 01305 262382; fax 01305 266412.

🚪 1.5 miles S of A35 between Dorchester and Puddletown.

🍴🍴 £25.

🛏 £45.

🛏 £70.

The village was Mellstock in Hardy's *Under the Greenwood Tree,* and the house was once two cottages, although now converted to hotel, with bedrooms tucked discreetly round the back in a modern extension. It is a good plan to find a tree of your own, under which to take tea – cream, of course. Nick Larby's cooking has been described as light on the fireworks but allowing the materials to speak for themselves. This is as it should be.

Westcountry dishes: smoked loin of pork with a cider and pink peppercorn sauce.

MAIDEN NEWTON
<u>R</u>
Petit Canard
Maiden Newton, DT2 0BE.
🍴19.00–20.45 (Tues-Sat).
Annual closure: 1st week Jan, 1 week Jun..
☎ **01300 320536.**
🍴🍴 £ 29.50.

The name is French, the Chapmans are Canadian, the cooking has the zip and zing of the New World (grilled kangaroo fillet with a truffle soufflé and mushroom sauce) and they admit that 'we are not overtly celebrating the bounty of the Westcountry, but use local ingredients if they are good.' We might hope that, in time, Westcountry Cooking would ensure that all local ingredients were good, and the Chapmans have found some that lend themselves to their individual treatment. They take lamb, goat, chicken and duck from the farms of four of their customers; they have two local ladies who grow vegetables and fruit for them; neighbours shoot pigeon and rabbits and bring them to the kitchen door; crayfish are supplied by Flowers Fish Farm near Shaftesbury; Denhay Farms produce bacon and ham; cheeses come up from Ticklemore in Totnes; and fish from Davy's Locker in West Bay. OK, so it's not heritage cookery – but who is sure we want that? It is getting close to that French concept of *cuisine de terroir.*

MILBORNE PORT
<u>H</u>
Old Vicarage
Sherbourne Road, Milborne Port, DT9 5AT.
🍴12.00–14.00 (Sun), 19.00–21.30 (Tues–Sat).
Annual closure: Jan.
☎ **01963 251117; fax 01963 251515.**
🍴🍴£17 (lunch), £24 (dinner).
🛏 £30.
🛏 £60.

This vicarage is so large that perhaps a bishop, or at least an archdeacon, was its tenant. Today, however, it is the Gnoyke family who provide comfortable hospitality and a certain humour: 'Dorset pheasant roasted to my Prussian grand-mother's recipe' is on the menu. 'She could not cook either,' is the comment. Guests may be relieved that the cooking is in the hands of Peter Talbot, and that fish from Cornwall gets an honourable place, as well as game supplied by Terry Dear in Yeovil and ham and pork from Denhay Farm. What might be all regional is balanced by produce brought down from Scotland: Argyll ham, smoked beef from Lorn, and Orkney sweet-cured herring are examples.

PLUSH
P
Brace of Pheasants
Plush, DT2 7RQ.
12.00–14.30, 19.00–21.45.
☎ 01300 348357.
£22.

The Brace started life, as the Knights will happily tell you, as two thatched cottages and a smithy. The conversion is 100 per cent: full of atmosphere and inglenooks. There's a Dining-Room, 'the Old Kitchen' for families (both non-smoking), the Bar, and the Hunters' Lodge (for skittles and weddings). Bar food is taken in any area; the Dining Room is the place for an extended meal. The formal menu is supplemented by any number of items on the daily blackboards. In common with many pub kitchens, and the grandest of restaurants too, they are where to look for the most exciting offers, be it fish off the boats, or excellent confections like lamb and rosemary pie. Thursday night is curry night – that old Westcountry custom. Oh, and the dog's called Bodger.

Westcountry dishes: lamb and rosemary pie; salmon with a saffron and scallop sauce.

POOLE

H

Mansion House

Thames Street, Poole, BH15 1JN.

🍴12.00–14.00 (Mon–Fri, Sun); 19.00–21.30 (Mon–Sat).

Annual closure: 27–30 Dec, 2–9 Jan.

☎ **01202 685666; fax 01202 665709.**

🍴🍴 £30.

🛏 £55.

🛏 £85.

Poole has grown so quickly in the last few years that you would be forgiven for thinking that houses like this no longer survive. But it does: and the panelled club room, comfort ad infinitum and some pleasing architecture give a substantial frame to fairly extravagant cookery. As Robert Leonard observes, his clientele includes many local businessmen, and they like hot steamed puddings and British items such as Lancashire hot pot and liver and bacon every bit as much as ragout of monkfish, tiger prawns and mussels with a Thai curry fish cream sauce. The kitchen runs parallel British and international tracks, and the fish and game cookery, for instance, is recommended.

Westcountry dishes: rabbit in cider with mushrooms; Brixham fish soup.

POWERSTOCK

P

Three Horseshoes Inn

Powerstock, DT6 3TF.

🍴12.00–14.00, 19.00–22.00.

☎ **01308 485328.; fax 01308 485577.**

🍴🍴 £18.50.

🛏 £30.

🛏 £40.

This pub specializes in fish cookery, from grilled sardines to local lobsters, with a middle course of squid with chilli and garlic if you wish. The range is great, and the handling assured. Meat-lovers will not be disappointed by the Beaminster bangers, or the Denhay ham, or a dish of wild rabbit with celery, bacon, shallots and cider sauce. Dorset lamb is another strong suit. All in all, an asset to the village.

SHAFTESBURY
R

La Fleur de Lys
25 Salisbury Street, Shaftesbury, SP7 8EL.
🍴 12.00–14.30 (Tues–Sat), 19.00–22.00 (Mon–Sat).
☎ 01747 853717.
🍴🍴 £26.

La Fleur de Lys is a pink lily, and it's found in a stable loft behind the street-front house. David Shepherd and his partners have translated their experience gained in larger, more worldly-wise kitchens into something very acceptable for this Dorset market town. It is sophisticated cooking, with an array of elements and ingredients in dishes like saddle of lamb baked in filo pastry with a mushroom mixture, roast garlic and a smoky bacon sauce, or asparagus on dauphinoise potatoes with shitake mushrooms and a garlic sauce. Not local in style, therefore, but materials display energy and loyalty in the sourcing.

SHERBORNE
R (WITH ROOMS)

Pheasants Restaurant
24 Greenhill, Sherborne, DT9 4EW.
🍴 12.00-14.00 (Tues-Sun), 18.30-22.00 (Tues-Sat).
Annual closure: 2 weeks mid Jan.
☎ 01935 815252.
🚍 at top of Sherborne High Street on A30 Yeovil to Salisbury road.
🍴🍴 £30.
🛏 £40.
🛎 £55.

There have been both Hardy and Wessex 'evenings' at this useful base for touring Hardy country, but from day to day, the kitchen adopts a more eclectic stance. The Overhills have enough faith in their suppliers to give a list of their names in each menu. Dishes do indeed spread their wings to the world: Scotch broth rubs shoulders with mushroom samosas. They also cook a meat not often seen in restaurants: goose. They take off the breast and serve it with black truffles, glazed onions and a port sauce.

STUDLAND
<u>H</u>
Manor House
Studland, BH19 3AU.
🍽 **12.00–14.00, 19.00–20.30.**
Annual closure: mid Dec–mid Jan.
☎ **01929 450288.**
🍽🍽 **£26.40.**
🛏 **£48 (incl. dinner).**
🛏 **£96 (incl. dinner).**

Brave the water on the Sandbanks car ferry across the mouth of Poole Harbour, then a few miles drive to this large manor house looking over Studland Bay. Breathtaking views, and just the place to let rip on whatever seafood they have to offer, be it crab, lobster, squid, sole, plaice, or cod.

STURMINSTER NEWTON

H

Plumber Manor

Sturminster Newton, DT10 2AF.

🍴 **19.30–21.00, and Sun lunch.**

Annual closure: Feb.

☎ **01258 472507; fax 01258 473370.**

🚗 **A357 from Sturminster Newton towards Sherborne, left to Hazelbury Bryan, then 2 miles on LHS.**

🍴🍴 **£23.50.**

🛏 **£70.**

🛏 **£90.**

The family has been here for ages, and the hotel has that relaxed, confident and unflurried feel of English country homes. The strengths of the cooking are perhaps English too: the meat and game are excellent, and sensitively bought and prepared. The puddings can be masterful.

Westcountry dishes: pork with cider.

SWANAGE

R

Galley

9 High Street, Swanage, BH19 2UN.

🍴 **18.45–21.30 (22.00 Sat).**

Annual closure: Nov, Jan, Feb.

☎ **01929 427299.**

🍴🍴 **£28.**

Fish and more fish is the recipe in this handsome converted Victorian shop with an intriguing octopus sculpture on the stoop. Nick Storer is not content to only cook, he grows his own soft fruits, asparagus, herbs and hop shoots (now there's a revived ingredient for the century's end). Fish is not messed about too much – always a good sign – and if meat is an essential for a hungry diner there is plenty of that available too. Mark particularly the game such as pheasant with garlic mash and port sauce, game pie with stout, or venison steak. Word has it that puddings may include steamed ones, or there is Dorset apple cake.

TARRANT MONKTON
P
Langton Arms
Tarrant Monkton, OT11 8RX.
🍴11.30–2.30 (Sun 12.00), 18.00–22.00 (Sun 21.30).
☎ 01258 830225; fax 01258 830053.
🍴🍴 £17.50.
🛏 £35.
🛎 £54.

Barbara and James Cossins have a farm which they run in tandem with this thatched pub in a thatched village. Bar food and a small bistro in the former stables and conservatory also run in parallel; and there is a printed menu supplemented by daily offerings. Monday night is fish and chip night, and on Thursday everyone eats steak, but otherwise it's a good plan to watch for game in season. If there is none, venison sausages are recommended. Come summer, into the garden for a barbecue, which suits the meats to perfection.

Westcountry dishes: **Somerset Brie filo parcel; Dorset apple cake.**

TRENT
P
Rose & Crown Inn
Trent, DT9 4SL.
🍴12.00–13.45, 19.00–21.00.
☎ 01935 850776.
🍴🍴 £15.

There is no doubting the Marion-Crawfords' commitment to their region. Several awards for Westcountry cheeses have been won and the blackboard displays a proud list of blue vinney, Somerset brie, Wedmore smoked Cheddar, Cornish yarg, farmhouse Cheddar and Tournegus. Their suppliers, too, are Dorset (or Somerset) men and women: fish from Poole, unpasteurized cream from Babcary, fruit and veg. from the village. The daily choices include some grand old dishes like boiled mutton and caper sauce (how often do you see that?), shepherds pie, spotted dick or jam roly-poly. Alternatively, there is an exotic streak that produces Louisiana blackened swordfish, lemon sole with a Canary Island 'mojo' sauce, Hungarian veal casserole, or beef enchilada. The common factor is that the food is fresh, cooked to order, and enjoyable.

Westcountry dishes: rabbit casseroled with cider and mushrooms; pork with a Somerset apple brandy sauce.

UPWEY
C
Upwey Wishing Well
Church Street, Upwey, DT3 5QE.
🕚10.30–18.00 (daily Mar–mid Dec; closed Mon–Tues Mar, Oct–Dec).
Annual closure: Dec–Mar.
☎ 01305 814470; fax 01305 813465.
🍴🍴 £10.75, unlicensed.

The Wishing Well once served cream teas to tourists but, since reconstruction and remodelling, has extended its business to plentiful lunches over a longer season appreciated by locals and visitors alike. Rare-breed, organically reared pork and lamb, Portland crab, farmed trout from Upwey itself, and venison supplied from Dorchester are essential ingredients in dishes like trout and spinach bake, venison casserole, or roast meats served for Sunday lunch. Afterwards, there are variations on the theme of British puddings: apple and mulberry crumble, queen of puddings, steamed ginger pudding to name but three.

Westcountry dishes: **Dorset apple cake.**

WAREHAM
H
Priory Hotel
Church Green, Wareham, BH20 4ND.
🍴 12.30-14.00, 19.30-22.00.
☎ 01929 551666; fax 01929 554519.
🍴🍴 £ 21.
🛏 £65.
🛌 £80.

Both buildings and garden make this a visit to remember.
The house really was a priory, and the dining-room lives up
to its name, the Abbot's Cellar. (The wine list, by way of
parenthesis, is excellent, including a Wimborne vintage
from Horton Vineyard.) Lots of ideas seem brimming in the
kitchen, but there is an English vein running through the
culinary mine, resulting in dishes like rib of beef with
asparagus, and a green peppercorn sauce, or oxtail with
leeks, or an honest ploughman's lunch (except here it is
monk's), or rack of venison with celeriac purée. The roasts
are well executed, and the fish carefully bought. Being on
the edge of town, the place feels like a country house.

WEST BAY
R
Riverside
West Bay, DT6 4EZ.
🍴 12.00–14.30, 18.30–21.00 (Tues–Sat, Sun lunch and
summer bank holidays).
Annual closure: Dec–Feb.
☎ 01308 422011.
🍴🍴 £20.

The Watsons used to run a post office in tandem with a café
on this site. Then Janet Watson became enthusiastic about
cooking more and better things and slowly the café took on
something of a restaurant (still with its feet firmly on the
ground). Of late, the post office moved to the village, and
the restaurant has probably won the tussle of the three faces

of Riverside. It is an exemplary fish restaurant, with excellent materials from oysters to shellfish to the finest white fish, sensibly treated so that flavours are not masked by over-fanciful treatments. The setting, the service and the bill at the end are people-friendly, and children are not discouraged. It's a holidaymaker's dream after a fretful day on the beach.

WEST BEXINGTON
H

Manor Hotel

West Bexington, DJ2 9DF.
🍴 12.00–13.30, 19.00–21.30.
☎ 01308 897616; fax 01308 897035.
🍴🍴 £25.
🛏 £47.
🛏 £80.

The house looks out to the sweep of Chesil Bank and water lapping over miles of pebbles. The Childs have managed over the years to make their hotel all things to all men, women and children, with a variety of food available at lots of different prices, and a sense of jolly welcome that makes it a cheerful spot to stay, or eat, or drink. The cooking is pretty lively too, with recipes and treatments springing out of a fertile brain that can summon up monkfish with cucumber raita or a red Thai chicken curry or salmon with a lime and avocado salsa. Materials come from closer to home, and they are also put to use in dishes that have stronger Dorset roots such as casserole of rabbit and ham or steak, kidney and oyster pie.

Westcountry dishes: exotic fruits and air dried Dorset ham with apricot chutney; cider-soused herrings; mussels with julienne of leeks, cider and cream; roast monkfish tail and Dorset ham.

WEYMOUTH
R
Mallams at the Quay

5 Trinity Road, Weymouth, DT4 8TJ.
🍴 **19.00–21.30 (Mon–Sat, & Sun May–Sept).**
☎ **01305 776757.**
🍴🍴 **£25.**

Stephen Gosson is happy to put the full range of Dorset seafood on the menu at his quayside restaurant: oysters from Abbotsbury, John Dory, brill, monkfish and cod on a single day, with salmon for good measure, as well as a few things with decidedly non-regional tiger prawns. Meat, too, gets a fair outing, with loin of pork with a poivrade sauce perhaps heading the list. It's rare-breed pork, and the customer is urged to ask about the breed before placing the order. Perhaps the exchanges go, 'No, I'll not have Saddleback today, I'll wait until you have Gloucester Old Spot.' Would that we could be so choosy. Stephen's variation on Dorset apple cake is also worth noting: it makes a change from those bits of sponge from a packet.

Westcountry dishes: local oysters grilled with garlic and Parmesan; Dorset apple cake Alaska.

WEYMOUTH
R
Perrys

4 Trinity Road, Weymouth, DT4 8TJ.
🍴**12.00-14.00 (Tues-Fri, & Sun), 19.00-21.30 (Mon-Sat & Suns in season).**
Annual closure: Christmas Day, Boxing Day and New Year's Day.
☎ **01305 785799.**
🍴🍴 **£22 (lunch); £28 (dinner).**

The Hodders also run the Mock Turtle restaurant in Dorchester, but Perrys has understandably a greater emphasis on fish, given its quayside location. Cornwall is the source of much of it, although the shellfish may come from Portland. The menu announces that they are a 'slow food' restaurant, so you may have to wait for the fish to be cooked. Sensible, though perhaps reflecting on the mindless impatience of many customers who seem to think that fish jumps out of the freezer into the microwave with never a pause for preparation.

Westcountry dishes: Portland crab bisque; Helford oysters; medallions of Dorset lamb with redcurrant jelly.

WIMBORNE
<u>H</u>
Beechleas
17 Poole Road, Wimborne, BH21 1QA.
(🍴)**19.30–21.30.**
Annual closure: 24 Dec–12 Jan.
☎ **01202 841684; fax 01202 849344.**
(🍴)(🍴) **£28.**
🛏 **£60.**
🛏 **£75.**

The original Georgian townhouse with its modern conservatory and walled garden has sprouted annexes in a coach house and in the lodge, a modern replica on the other side of the car park. Comfort is extreme. Dining goes on in the conservatory, cooking on an Aga. That alone does not signify Westcountry, but it sets a certain tone, reinforced by knowledge that much of the organic produce used in the kitchen comes from Hockey's Farm in Fordingbridge – and Denhay pork and ham as well. It's wise to leave space for the third, sweet, course, when the eye is likely to be seduced by more than just one item.

Westcountry dishes: pork in cider, cream and apple sauce; apple, sultana and cinnamon crumble.

Gloucestershire

(INCLUDING BRISTOL)

Introduction

Gloucestershire is the very edge of the South West, and there are many aspects that pull away from the region rather than gathering it in. The river Severn cuts through the county, so that the Forest of Dean, on the far side, with its ancient iron workings and coal mines, sometimes appears more of Wales than England. The Cotswolds, the north-south spine, thrust towards the Midlands, tilting the emphasis to Oxfordshire and Warwick. The county splits too between Bristol to the south and Gloucester and Cheltenham to the north.

Bristol has been a magnet for produce from all the South West, and South Wales as well, and its long tradition of sea trade has brought into the region ingredients and methods from foreign parts. 'I inquired if that little town could consume such a quantity of veal; they told me the boats were ready in the river to buy for Bristol,' wrote Arthur Young during his tour of the district in the Georgian period. Today, its restaurants and wine merchants have a similarly galvanic effect.

Although sea fish now come into the county from Devon and Cornwall, the Severn supplies two rarely seen delicacies: elvers, the fry of eel that run for a short season, are mostly exported to countries that appreciate them better, but can still be found at a few lucky spots; and lampreys, the death of king Henry I, that were baked into a pie by the burghers of Gloucester for an annual royal gift, and which are valued more in Bordeaux than here. So long was there an association of Gloucester and lampreys that the Tsarina Catherine the Great had heard of it in the eighteenth century and commanded that a pie should be sent her in St Petersburg. The Severn is in fact tidal a long way up its estuary, and used to support a vigorous and varied fishery, from sturgeon and salmon to halibut and conger eel. It also provided waterfowl, from herons to cormorants, that fishermen would make into high-flavoured, if not appetizing, pies.

The high ground of the Cotswolds supported sheep, the pastures of the vale fed cattle: double and single Gloucester cheeses on the one hand, the great wool merchants' churches of Cotswold market towns and the mills of the valleys around Stroud and Nailsworth on the other. Cheese brings Gloucestershire into the Somerset and Devon ambit, as surely as does cider production in the orchards towards Worcester and Hereford. And the Gloucester Old Spot pig, a breed now treasured by several organic pork producers, offers a further connection. The pig was the people's meat. Cornish and Devonshire cookery revolved in large part around it – game was for the gentry, following recipes and methods of wider origins – and Gloucestershire and many other agricultural counties shared this preoccupation. Gloucester hams were once particularly esteemed because of the pigs' diet of beech mast

These early characteristics may be hard to identify in cookery today. Gloucestershire is part of the metropolitan nexus, its population growing by leaps and bounds at weekends. Restaurants and cooks pursue city fashions and enthusiasms, rather than drawing on the inspiration of place. Bed and breakfasts are generally of the cordon bleu, superior sort, occupying former manor houses and rectories.

Some local dishes

Brawn
Lardy cake
Oldbury tarts
Clifton puffs
Fried elvers
Elver pie
Toasted cheese and ale
Market casserole of pork and apples
Tewsbury saucer batter
Speech House pudding
Cheltenham pudding
Cheltenham cakes
Roast lamb stuffed with apples and cider
Tewkesbury mustard
Gloucester sauce
Gloucestershire boiled cake

BIRDLIP
R (WITH ROOMS)
Kingshead House

Birdlip, GL4 8JH.

🍴 **12.15–14.00 (Tues–Fri & Sun), 19.30–21.45 (Tues–Sat).**

Annual closure: 25 Dec–28 Jan.

☎ **01452 862299.**

🚪 **1/4 mile out of Birdlip on B4070 to Stroud .**

🍴🍴 **£31.50.**

🛏 **£35.**

🛏 **£60.**

Judy Knock has been creating food, and Warren her husband looking after the customers and the wine cellar, at this double-fronted Cotswold stone house for a number of years. Her style takes many forms, often reminiscent of French country cooking – showcased in regional wine and food evenings with carefully researched suppers. But from a varied number of sources, the amalgam encountered at Kingshead becomes particularly British. How many nations accept without quiver swede and ginger soup, aubergine pilaff with a light curry sauce, and beef with wild mushrooms on the same menu? We have a remarkable culinary tolerance. This pleasingly magpie tendency goes hand in hand with an eye alert to good produce and its possibilities.

With an excellent cellar of wine and beer, this is a good place to sample Double Gloucester from Smarts of Churcham, or Single Gloucester or Stinking Bishop from Charles Martell. Gloucester cheese and ale is a form of English rarebit. Cheese is baked with beer and mustard until it is bubbling and runny, it is then poured over slices of toast and served with pickles and beer.

Westcountry dishes: pheasant with prunes and cider; rabbit casseroled in cider; Devon squab; hot Gloucester salad (a salad with topping of grilled Double Gloucester); cheese and ale.

BRISTOL
R
Bells Diner
1 York Road, Bristol, BS6 5QB.
🍴**12.30–14.00, 19.00–21.30 (not Sat lunch & Sun dinner)**
Annual closure: last week Aug, 3 days at Christmas & Easter.
☎ **0117 924 0357; fax 0117 924 4280.**
🍴🍴 **£23.**

Once a grocer's shop (see the shelves and panelling), now a creative kitchen with a forward-looking wine list and lots of happy customers. They are also non-smokers (at least, if they do smoke, they 'take refuge in the reception area'). The list of suppliers nails their colours to the mast: J.R. Twine for organic cream, Hicks Gate Farm for meat and eggs, Wing of St Mawes for fish, Morf's Herbs in Portishead for salads and herbs. Cornish Yarg, Beenleigh Blue, Sharpham, and Keen's Cheddar jostle for room on the British cheese plate. The style of cooking is modern: for which read a cross between American West Coast, French, Italian peasant, with a drop of English in sweet-sour combos or airy stodge at pudding time. It's a good mixture: smoked mackerel fish cakes with gooseberry relish; brawn with salsa verde; sea bass with saffron mash; sticky toffee pudding.

BRISTOL
R
Hunt's Restaurant
26 Broad Street, Bristol, BS1 2HG.
🍴**12.00–14.00, 19.00–22.00 Tues–Sat, except Sat lunch.**
Annual closure: 1 week Easter, August, & Christmas.
☎ **0117 9265580.**
🍴🍴 **£30.**

Andy Hunt's menu, presented in this small city-centre restaurant, is a fine example of English taste. It may be informed by French cookery – when was England not? –

with marquises, parfaits, and gratins dotted about, but the composition of flavours, and the origins of the main ingredients is all our own. Baked goats' cheese, sweet onion marmalade and baby leeks; Trelough duck breast with spiced plums; Cornish crab gratin with a fricassee of monkfish, scented with saffron; venison with sweet dill gherkins, tarragon and sour cream; crème brûlée (and that, despite its name, is English) with rhubarb and elderflower; or apple and cinnamon tart with butterscotch sauce and a geranium spoom: these are the sort of recipes that inform a new sense of locality.

BRISTOL

<u>R</u>

Markwick's

43 Corn Street, Bristol, BS1 1HT.

🍴12.00–14.00, 19.00–22.30 (Tues–Sat except Sat lunch).

Annual closure: 2 weeks Aug, Christmas & Easter.

☎ 0117 9262658.

🍴🍴 £21.50.

Stephen and Judy Markwick's cellar was once a bank vault: the grilles are there to prove it. It has converted handsomely and Stephen produces meals worth any overdraft. His style is unfussy yet delivering bags of flavour with a marked emphasis on good shopping. Try the Provençal fish soup for a welcome surprise in Bristol, or the home-made venison sausages sent out to Heritage Foods to be smoked. Stephen has spent many years in Bristol, Helford and Dartmouth, so knows well his lines of supply. One 'local' dish he often cooks is a recent tradition, but worth the detour. George Perry-Smith developed his salmon layered with ginger and currants, then wrapped in pastry before baking, from an old medieval recipe while he was running the Hole in the Wall restaurant in Bath in the 1950s. It has since entered the repertoire of many of his pupils, and bids fair to become a 'Westcountry' dish, though there is only recent practice to link it to the region. Whatever the history, it is delicious.

Westcountry dishes: George Perry–Smith's salmon in pastry with ginger and currants.

CHIPPING CAMPDEN

H

Seymour House

The High Street, Chipping Campden, GL55 6AH.

🍽 **12.00–14.30, 19.00–22.30.**

☎ **01386 840429; fax 01386 840369.**

🍽🍽 **£18.50 (lunch), £27.50 (dinner).**

🛏 **£65.**

🛏 **£90.**

It seems unfair that the Cotswolds should have all the eggs of beauty in their basket, and that the High Street, Chipping Campden should wear a face that launched a million postcards, but Seymour House reaps the benefits. Mellow stone meets fine wood panelling. In the outside-in conservatory restaurant with a vine sinuously winding its way to the ceiling lantern, diners are treated to food with an Italian tilt, although materials are steadfastly local. Puddings veer more towards British inspiration, and that tipsy cake mentioned below is an instance. Just what ties it to Somerset is unclear. Tipsy cake, which is called tipsy parson in America, is a variant, perhaps more alcoholic, of trifle.

Westcountry dishes: Somerset tipsy cake using apple brandy, clotted cream and fresh fruits.

CORSE LAWN

H

Corse Lawn House

Corse Lawn, GL19 4LZ.

🍽 **12.00–14.00, 19.00–22.00.**

☎ **01452 780771/479; fax 01452 780840.**

🍽🍽 **Restaurant, £20 (lunch), £30 (dinner); bistro £20.**

🛏 **£70.**

🛏 **£100.**

Over twenty years, the Hine family has refurbished and
expanded this tall red-brick house standing on the side of a
mile-long lawn or common. At its front door there is a
handsome pond. This was an early car wash: for horse
drawn carriages, not Mondeos. New building has greatly
expanded the original, making a comfortable hotel, with a
bistro as well as a restaurant, a fine wine cellar, and upwards
of 20 bedrooms, set in large gardens. Tim Earley's and Baba
Hine's style of cookery is that country mixture of traditional
with an angle, plus international eclectic. Hence a menu
may offer braised tongue with piquant sauce and flageolet
beans (traditional), alongside a piece of cod served with a
Japanese tempura batter and an oriental salad. Sources of a
cooking style may allowably be much wider than those of
the materials used in the kitchen. A list of some local
ingredients underlines the wealth of the region. Scallops,
mussels, cockles, oysters, hake and mullet come up from
the south-west peninsula; salmon from the Severn and Wye;
lamb, beef, and pork from local farmers and butchers;
pigeon, hare and rabbits from sportsmen; samphire, wild
mushrooms, hop shoots and wild garlic from hedges, banks
and cliffs; the usual cornucopia of fruit and veg.; and a slate
of fine cheeses that measure up to many other countries.
Links with growers and suppliers take time to develop: a
kitchen such as Corse Lawn's does not happen overnight.
But once it has been established, it acts like a dynamo to
keep the current of innovation and action ever lively.

Westcountry dishes: guinea fowl with cider and apples;
lamb with hop shoots and wild garlic; home-smoked
mackerel with Tewkesbury mustard.

DRYBROOK

R

Cider Press

The Cross, Drybrook, GL17 9EB.

🍽19.00 (19.30 winter) Wed–Sat.

Annual closure: first 2–3 weeks Jan.

☎ 01594 544472.

🍽🍽 £26.

As a traveller progresses into the country beyond the river Severn, he or she may think that England is cast off and Wales beckons. But the Forest of Dean, which makes up this wedge of Gloucestershire, is English still, and mighty interesting into the bargain, with plenty of relics of the iron smelting and coalmining that used to be the source of the wealth of the region. The Cider Press presumably made the liquid that fuelled hard work in wood and mine, but now is converted into a small but well-filled restaurant where fish and shellfish from the Bristol Channel and beyond are an important centrepiece of Christopher Challener's skills, and where much work has been done to highlight the culinary heritage of the district. There is escabeche, for instance: a variation on hot-pickled fish, originally Spanish and Portuguese, but brought back to England by the sailors of the seventeenth century who ventured on the Spanish Main. Then there is Cotswold lamb, which is a loin of lamb rolled and stuffed with apple, sage, cloves, garlic and ginger, roasted and basted with apple wine. This is inspired by a Gloucestershire tradition, but is served with aubergine and tomato ragout, giving it a Mediterranean tilt. Scallops are served with samphire (something of Wales in that), and there is roast saddle of kid with tarragon. Kid was a famous Welsh delicacy: just be sure you are not served goat. Unlike lamb and mutton, kid does not benefit from age! The cheeseboard looks to each side of the border, with Welsh and Westcountry offerings.

Westcountry dishes: Cotswold lamb; pheasant roasted with butter, apples, cider and cream; scallops with samphire.

HAZLETON
<u>B&B</u>
Windrush House
Hazleton, GL54 4EB.
🍴19.30.
Annual closure: Dec–Jan.
☎ 01451 860364.
🍴🍴 £23.
🛏 £22.
🛏 £40.

People report glowingly of Mrs Sidney Harrison's cooking at this modern house on the edge of the hamlet of Hazleton. A quite simple menu is cooked each day, usually with meat as the centrepiece, where the watchword is that each item is to the point and at its best. It's good to see Gloucester Old Spot being used to such advantage, and cheese lovers will welcome good Double Gloucester and Stinking Bishop as a finish to their meals.

Westcountry dishes: **Old Spot sausages; Old Spot pork with mustard sauce; lamb baked in hay.**

MORETON-IN-MARSH

R

Annie's

3 Oxford Street, Moreton-in-Marsh, GL56 0LA.

🍽19.00–21.30 (Mon-Sat).

Annual closure: end Jan–beginning Feb.

☎ **01608 651981.**

🍽🍽 £35.

A pretty Cotswold-stone cottage bedecked with flowers is home to David Ellis' cooking, while Anne makes everybody welcome, giving a happy sense of belonging to dining out. As well as stove-top and fast-baked food familiar to restaurants everywhere, like tiger prawns wrapped in filo, or venison fillet with a green peppercorn sauce, David Ellis is a dab hand at slow-cooked pies: how about chicken, bacon and mushroom? This gift is extended to desserts with a traditional bent such as ratafia (layered cream and macaroons), treacle tart, toffee pudding, or fruit crumble and custard.

NORTHLEACH

H

Wheatsheaf Hotel

West End, Northleach, GL54 3EZ.

🍽12.00–14.30, 18.30–21.30.

☎ **01452 860244; fax 01451 861037.**

🔲 where A429 and A40 cross.

🍽🍽 £21.

🛏 £39.

🛏 £52.

An old English supper at the Wheatsheaf included a Gloucestershire squab pie, lamb - with apples and spices - although other dishes, excluding of the cider syllabub, were drawn from regions outside the Westcountry. Generally, the kitchen works in mainstream pub and country hotel vein: tiger prawns and avocados getting as much of the limelight as ingredients from the locality, but people enjoy the atmosphere and the consistency of performance.

PAINSWICK

<u>R</u>

Country Elephant

New Street, Painswick, GL6 6XH.

🍴12.00–14.00. 19.00–22.00 (Tues–Sat, Sun lunch on
bank holiday weekends and Mothering Sunday).
Annual closure: three weeks Jan.
☎ **01452 813564.**
🍴🍴 £18 (lunch), £25 (dinner) .

Robert Rees trained with the Roux brothers in London. His
style has the sophistication and breadth that stems from that
sort of background. Not to say he doesn't try the odd
stargazey pie, though he notes it is none too popular. Lack
of wild acclaim may derive from people's fear that they will
be greeted by a row of beady fish eyes glaring at them from
the pastry topping. They shouldn't worry. Mussel and
whisky soup is another Rees variation on local materials, as
is ragout of artichokes and asparagus with apples and cider.
The Country Elephant is nicely informal, stretching into a
garden on summer days, yet offering food a notch above the
norm. The true enthusiast can try fresh snails with almonds
and wild mushrooms, in a Chartreuse sauce. In the West,
they are known as 'wallfish', and are grown commercially at
Curry Rivel, near Langport in Somerset. Other than their
being essential components in various old medical receipts,
I have not found much evidence of their popularity in
English kitchen. It took the French to introduce them to us
as desirable. The Miner's Arms at Priddy in the Mendips
based its considerable reputation in the '50s and '60s on
snails collected by schoolboys anxious to earn the landlord's
bounty. Nowadays, they are more systematic in their efforts
to ensure supply.

RANGEWORTHY

H

Rangeworthy Court

Church Lane, Rangeworthy, BS17 5ND.

🍴 12.00–13.45, 19.00–21.30.

☎ 01454 228347; fax 01454 228945.

🍴🍴 £23.

🛏 £53.

🛏 £68.

The house was built in the seventeenth century by the Lord Chief Justice Sir Matthew Hale. Many original features remain; the swimming pool is new. Visitors can have the relaxed comfort of country living while a few minutes' drive from the city of Bristol. Cookery avoids over-elaboration, allowing the main ingredients their say in dishes like pigeon breast on mashed parsnip and potato, or mackerel fillets with lemon-scented spinach leaves. Meat dishes may reflect some of the substance and flavour of the Judge's times: no stinting on the gravy.

Westcountry dishes: roast loin of pork with rich cider and apple gravy.

THORNBURY

H

Thornbury Castle

Castle Street, Thornbury, BS12 1HH.

🍴 12.00–14.00, 19.00–21.30 (21.00 Sun, 22.00 Sat).

Annual closure: 4 days in Jan.

☎ 01454 281182.; fax 01454 416188.

🍴🍴 £28.25 (lunch), £44.25 (dinner).

🛏 £95.

🛏 £145.

The last castle to be built in England makes a fine hotel, with four-posters, tower-rooms and bags of atmosphere, as well as succulent luxury. It is also one of the few restaurants in Britain with a vineyard at its gate. It serves its own wine as aperitif. Kitchens cooking for this sort of establishment do not really go in for regional food, although the materials may be, and are here, exemplary. That said, Steven Black cooks a first-rate treacle tart with Cornish clotted cream, and his breast of duck coated in honey, then served with a cider vinegar sauce, or his hot roasted apple with honey sauce and served with a hazelnut ice cream show what may be done with materials to hand.

UPPER ODDINGTON

P

Horse & Groom Inn

Upper Oddington, GL56 0XH.

🍴12.00–14.00, 18.30–21.30.

☎ 01451 830584.

🚌 2 miles E of Stow-on-the-Wold on A436 to Chipping Norton.

🍴🍴 £20.

🛏 £40.

🛎 £55.

The pub has been completely done over in the first months of the Souths' tenure, with bedrooms to follow soon after, to create a sparkling version of the Cotswold inn, and food and wines to match. Ingredients are drawn from wide horizons: crab may be from Cromer, oysters from Scotland, but there is a nucleus of Westcountry suppliers with elderflower pressé, fruit and vegetables, and free range eggs from farms in the village, Somerset brie filling long, satisfying lunchtime baguettes, and smoked fish and meat from Hugh Forestier-Walker's Minola Smokehouse near Lechlade.

Westcountry dishes: **pork in cider sauce.**

Somerset

Introduction

'The markets are very good here of all sorts of provision
flesh and fish ... great plenty and pretty reasonable,' wrote
the seventeenth-century traveller Celia Fiennes about Bath.
She went on, 'the chargeableness of Bath is the lodgings
and the firing, the faggots being very small.' Polite about
this long-fashionable resort, she thought less of the rural
south: 'generally a good fruitfull country,' but, 'no good
accomodation for people of fashion, the Country people
being a clounish rude people.'

Away from the metropolitan fringe of Bath and Bristol,
the towns were once centres of manufacture: gloves at Yeovil
and Taunton, horsehair at Bruton, crepe at Shepton Mallet,
lace at Chard, linen at Crewkerne. Much of this disappeared
with the Industrial Revolution, leaving a few primary indus-
tries such as brick making on the Severn shore, coal mining
in Radstock and lead mining in the Mendips. Relics are the
leather and footwear factories of Glastonbury and Street.
Daniel Defoe, author of *Robinson Crusoe*, assessed
Somerset's value a few years after Celia Fiennes had ridden
through: lush grasslands a source of beef for London; the
uplands a source of ponies and horses for the copers of
Staffordshire and Leicestershire, who sold them on for cart
and coach; and Cheddar cheese, 'the greatest, and the best
of the kind in England'.

Cow & Gate and Horlicks are two companies whose
wealth was founded on the produce identified by Defoe,
while the south facing slopes of the Mendips, with rich soil,
have offered great opportunity for market gardening and
intensive cultivation. Early strawberries, vegetables for
Bristol, and now vines have been some of their specialities.
Market gardening and orcharding has also been established
in the Vale of Taunton: again, south facing slopes (this time
the Quantocks), rich soil and sheltered climes. Taunton
strawberries are often earlier and last longer than any
others.

Another feather in Taunton's cap is cider. Coates was the
first commercial maker, founded in the 1920s, before which

production was concentrated in small farms. Today, there are fewer farmhouse producers than in Devon but greater emphasis on using varieties of apples grown only for cider.

There is a rich diversity of restaurants, pubs, hotels and other places cooking and serving food. In part this is encouraged by the concentration of wealth and incoming travellers to Bath and Bristol, but the rest of the county is also well served. This trade has generated in its turn an infrastructure of growers and suppliers, so that Somerset is not lacking in fine ingredients, even if memories of an earlier regional style are somewhat attenuated.

Some local dishes:

Priddy oggies
Pickled walnuts
Somerset stew
Bath polonies
Bath chaps
Braised lamb
Apple pudding
Bath buns
Bath Olivers
Sally Lunn buns
Cheese straws
Cattern cakes
Somerset fritters
Easter cakes
Dumpsie-dearie jam

ANSFORD

<u>H</u>

Bond's

Ansford, Castle Cary, BA7 7JP.

🍴12.00–14.00, 19.00–21.30.

Annual closure: 1 week Christmas.

☎ **01963 350464.**

🚪 **on A371, 400 yards from Castle Cary station.**

🍴🍴 £25.

🛏 £38.

🛏 £60.

It looks as if it might have been a rectory, though reputedly it was a stop for coach and horses on their way through deep south-Somerset lanes. For sure, the hedge-topped walls, neighbouring barns and pastures fly every flag of country living, even if the railway is but a hop and skip away. The Bonds are energetic and hospitable, Yvonne something of an advocate of Westcountry cooking. On the set menu, she has 'Cheese of the Day', often something local like the Capricorn goats' cheese from Crewkerne, 'creamier than the French varieties', she says. Asked if she ever cooks Westcountry dishes, she answers, 'Yes, but my own,' citing a puff-pastry box filled with Cheddar asparagus, with a tarragon and lemon butter as example. Or she might have cited butterbean and bacon soup using Sandridge Farm bacon ('No water!' is her comment), or venison carpaccio. The cooking is exuberant: those country lanes may have their use as running track to burn off the excess.

APPLEY
P
Globe Inn
Appley, TA21 0HJ.
🍴**12.00–14.00, 19.00–22.00 (closed Mon lunch).**
☎ **01823 672327.**
🚪 **junction 27 northbound on M5, then N on A38 for 4 miles to sign to Greenham Appley; junction 26 southbound, then S on A38 to sign for Greenham and Appley.**
🍴🍴 **£15.**

Afficionados of Cotleigh beer from Wiveliscombe, or farmhouse cider, can be sure of getting them in this country pub with a good name for food as well as a cheerful atmosphere that avoids too much of the green welly and Range Rover touch. The printed menu is a canter through world cookery: pork with Thai spices, lamb curry, chilli con carne, duck with plum sauce, but the daily dishes on the blackboard may go straighter to the heart of local materials and Westcountry cooking.

AXBRIDGE
H
Oak House
The Square, Axbridge, BS26 2AP.
🍴**12.00–14.15, 19.00–21.15.**
☎ **01934 732444; fax 01934 733112.**
🍴🍴 **£16.60.**
🛏 **£42.**
🛏 **£57.**

Though a city-centre hotel (were Axbridge a city), Oak House is a conversion of two adjoining cottages. The bistro to the hotel is called Piggy's, but what's in a name? A trio of Axbridge sausages may be what the wandering mind will turn to after hearing the name, but they will as probably be venison, or lamb, mint and rosemary as pig. Cheddar supplies cheese, strawberries and now, wines. It truly is a little hot-spot, benefiting from its micro-climate. The menu is surprisingly lively for a small market town in deepest Somerset, with a fair deal for vegetarians as well.

BARWICK
H
Little Barwick House
Barwick, BA22 7TD.
🍴19.00–21.00 (Mon–Sat, residents only Sun).
Annual closure: Christmas, New Year.
☎ 01935 423902; fax 01935 420908.
🖳 driving S, turn left off A37 Yeovil–Dorchester road at first roundabout, then 400 yards on left.
🍴🍴 £31.50.
🛏 £52.
🛌 £76.

Georgian dower houses, Little Barwick is one of these, are much the same as rectories: the comfort of country living without the overpowering magnificence. Veronica Colley's cooking might be described in the same fashion: all the skill of a professional chef, but comforting and encouraging, not pretentious. Many of her favourite dishes are exotic – guinea fowl marinated in Thai herbs and spices is one – but she is good at game cookery, and the hungry can go for 'pie of the week, made with Veronica's excellent shortcrust pastry', or a rack of Taunton Vale lamb with mint and cucumber sauce. Fish, too, is a strength, supplied from day-boats by Samways at West Bay.

Westcountry dishes: medallions of Melbury venison; Lyme Bay fish stew.

BATH

H
Bath Spa Hotel
Sydney Road, Bath, BA2 6JF.
🍽️**12.00–14.00, 18.00–22.00 (Alfresco); 18.00–22.00 &
Sunday lunch (Vellore).**
☎ **01225 444424; fax 01225 444006.**
🍽️🍽️ **£25 (Alfresco), £45 (Vellore).**
🛏️ **£129.**
🛏️ **£149.**

Imagine the nurses who used to occupy this glorious place
as a hostel! No thought of that today, steering a gentle curve
through the high perimeter wall, past cedared lawns to the
impressive pile that houses a many-chandeliered Vellore
restaurant for dinners (and breakfast) and the Alfresco
Colonnade, which is the slightly less formal area for lunch
and lighter (or cheaper) eating. Jonathan Fraser proclaims at
the head of his menu that his style mixes the 'Far East with
the Mediterranean and Old England', so the Westcountry is
perhaps in minor key in much-elaborated dishes such as the
dim sum of tiger prawns, pork and coriander with chow
chow and sweet ginger sauce. Some may even have difficulty
getting round the menu descriptions. That said, the fish is
from inshore boats, and there is an enjoyment of dumplings
(with a scrag of lamb, smoked bacon and beans, or with
lamb and root vegetables), both of which speak of feet on
the ground. Meals have been very soundly cooked, and as a
retreat from the hurly-burly of Bath it is unparalleled.

BATH

R
Hole in the Wall
16 George Street, Bath, BA1 2EH.
🍽️**12.00–14.00, 18.00–23.00, Mon–Sat.**
☎ **01225 425242.**
🍽️🍽️ **£26.**

There has been a succession of cooks and proprietors at this
restaurant, each contributing their lustre to a famous name.

What was once a picturesque cellar is now an intriguing combination of stone-toned original and gleaming modernity. The latest owners, for the past three years or so, have been Chris and Gunna Chown, who began, and continue, their hotel-restaurant at Plas Bodegroes in North Wales. Chris Chown was one of those new-wave British chefs who embraced most enthusiastically the idea of local food, local supplies, yet with an outward- and forward-looking style of cooking. This approach has rubbed off here too, with Eric le Pin in the kitchen. Flavours are assertive, whether coconut milk and coriander with turbot, or a tart cherry sauce with duck breast, monkfish with star anise or a foie gras terrine with red onion marmalade. While the style of cookery has little root in the locality, the materials certainly do, and freshness and impeccable sourcing is guaranteed.

BATH
R
Pump Room, Milburns Restaurant
Stall Street, Bath, BA1 1LZ.
🍴**12.00–14.30 (9.30–16.30/17.30 for light meals); open for dinner during high season.**
Annual closure: Dec 25/26.
☎ **01225 444477; fax b01225 447979.**
🍴🍴**£15.95.**

There has been a string trio or quartet playing in these columned halls for many years – before even I, as a boy, was brought wonderingly on half-days from school to have a cup of tea in comfort after all the rationing and ravages of war. They still play today, and there is a pianist at lunchtime. Milburns, who cater at many national museums or public sites, have made a good fist of coping cheerfully and elegantly with the tourists. Lunch is a creative affair: modern recipes of the sort that have made insitutional catering better than it was. Either side of the main meal are the moments to grasp a Bath bun or a cream tea: for some, the epitome of the city.

BATH

H

Queensberry Hotel

Russel Street, Bath, BA1 2QF.

🍽 **12.00–14.00, 19.00–22.00.**

Annual closure: 1 week Christmas.

☎ **01225 447928; fax 01225 446065.**

🍽🍽 **£15 (lunch), £30 (dinner).**

🛏 **£89.**

🛎 **£110.**

Below this most elegant town-house hotel, provided with every object any Bath visitor could ever require, is the Olive Tree restaurant. It may be the hotel's resource, but it has a life beyond that of catering merely for residents and their guests. The lively menu takes the Mediterranean as chief inspiration – why else call it the Olive Tree? This does not exclude the purely regional, for example a Cornish crab and saffron tart, or any of the excellent fish that forms an important part of the daily offerings.

BEERCROCOMBE

B&B

Frog Street Farm

Beercrocombe, TA3 6AF.

🍽 **19.00.**

Annual closure: Nov–Mar.

☎ **01823 480430.**

🍽🍽 **£15 (unlicensed).**

🛏 **£27.**

🛎 **£50.**

Frog Street is still a working farm and Mr Henry Cole is a racehorse trainer whose pupils lend thoroughbred tone to the surrounding paddocks. The house itself is older than its regular front may imply: hidden behind are beamed ceilings from the fifteenth century, Jacobean panelling and cavernous fireplaces. Reports have it the chief attraction of the farm is the welcoming personality of Mrs Coles and her excellent cooking. The content of meals is agreed between guest and cook and the style of their cookery is that happy compromise between art and nature that is English cooking at its best.

Westcountry dishes: pheasant in Somerset brandy; Somerset pork cooked in cider sauce.

BRUTON
R
Truffles

95 High Street, Bruton, BA10 0AR.
🍴12.00–14.00 (Sun), 19.00–22.00 (Tues–Sat).
Annual closure: 2 weeks late Jan.
☎ **01749 812255.**
🍴🍴 £20 (lunch), £28 (dinner).

A decade at this small restaurant was celebrated by the Bottrills during 1997. Martin Bottrill's mind is too lively to confine himself to immediate horizons and there is a definite eastern tint to some of his offerings: mussels Goan-style and pork with an oriental sauce are two instances. Nonetheless, local materials are given fair outings and the way in which the menu changes completely every month means that seasons are reflected in the food that is produced.

COMBE HAY
P
Wheatsheaf

Combe Hay, BA2 7EG.
🍴12.00–14.00, 18.30–21.30.
Annual closure: Christmas Day & Boxing Day.
☎ **01225 833504.**
🍴🍴 £16.
🛏 £40.
🛏 £70.

On the printed menus, suppliers are able to take advertising space: this may inform the customer as well as gain business. The food here is certainly enterprising, the pub very busy. It benefits from its surroundings, the gardens, and the view. Of all that is cooked, perhaps the game in season and the pies that come out steaming all the year round are the best bet. They stock Combe Hay wine, grown directly behind the inn, as well as Mumford, another Bath vintage.

DULVERTON
H
Ashwick House
Dulverton, TA22 9QD.
🍽 12.30–13.45 Sun only; 19.15–20.30.
☎ 01348 323868.
🚗 off B3223 Dulverton–Lynton road.
🍽🍽 £25.
🛏 £48.
🛏 £96.

The lawns swoop down to a lake from the terrace of this Edwardian country house and the attentive guest will be rewarded with a view of wildlife trotting, waddling or sneaking its way to the water's edge for refreshment. Meanwhile, Richard Sherwood will have finished writing an individual menu for each party staying the night. It may skirt round most local fauna but nonetheless gives fair reflection of Exmoor farming (and shooting, too). The kitchen's tendency is towards simplicity: letting the main ingredient speak for itself. While laverbread is usually thought a South Wales speciality, it is found on both sides of the Bristol Channel and is sold in the markets of north Devon and the Somerset coast. The suffix 'bread' has nothing to do with bread, but is an Englishing of the Welsh 'brith'. The moorland whortleberries are called hurtleberries or blaeberries in other parts of England. The great Exmoor novel *Lorna Doone* talks of a character being 'laid on a bank of whortleberries.' They make a grand summer fruit pie. The apple brandy sauce that Richard Sherwood cooks for his pork fillet is made of nothing so foreign as Calvados, but the Somerset Royal Cider Brandy created by Julian Temperley near Martock.

Westcountry dishes: pork fillet with apple brandy sauce; laverbread (for breakfast); whortleberry pie (in the summer).

DUNSTER
<u>C</u>
Tea Shoppe
3 High Street, Dunster, TA24 6SF.
🍴**12.00–15.00 (all week from Mar, weekends winter season), 19.00–21.00 (Fri & Sat).**
Annual closure: Jan.
☎ **01643 821304.**
🍴🍴 **£12.50.**

The price given here is for a full meal, but the Tea Shoppe offers lots of things at lower prices, for a smaller investment of time and trouble. It is open for light meals, good cream teas and the like from 10 o'clock in the morning. What Carver Doone (the villain of *Lorna Doone*) had to do with venison casserole, no-one is quite sure, perhaps he ate double helpings before some more rapine and pillage in seventeenth-century Exmoor. Pam Goldsack's Somerset savoury pudding is also interesting: this is a bread and butter pudding, but with fried sausage and tomatoes instead of raisins, a cheese topping and a savoury custard that is baked in just the same way as the one we all love for a sweet course. She remarked that she found a very similar recipe in an Italian regional cookery book. The Goldsacks' list of suppliers is a fine roll-call: Burrow Hill cider, Cricket Malherbie for cheese and dairy products and chicken, organic meat from Gerald David, Heal Farm for organic pork and sausages, and Mr Hoskins for venison and local game. Would that all tea shoppes made the effort.

Westcountry dishes: Somerset savoury pudding; pork cooked in cider with apples and leeks; apple cake; treacle tart; Carver Doone venison casserole.

EAST COKER
<u>B&B</u>
Holywell House

Holywell, East Coker, BA22 9NQ.
🍴19.30.
Annual closure: Christmas & New Year.
☎ 01935 862612; fax 01935 863035.
🚗 **turning signed to East Coker off A30, 2 miles W of Yeovil.**
🍴🍴 £17 (unlicensed).
🛏 £35.
🛏 £60.

Jackie and Ronald Somerville tell their guests that this four-square Ham stone house was once the miller's home, and the mill sluice figured in Thomas Hardy's story *A Tragedy of Two Ambitions*. Add East Coker's associations with T.S. Eliot, and the literary tourist's cup runneth over. Our interest is more mundane. The house has been luxuriously converted to take guests: order, good taste and fine furnishing abound. The garden – picked as one of the most interesting in Somerset, thanks to Ronald Somerville's exertions – provides produce a-plenty for Jackie to cook with, and she joins the home-grown to the carefully sourced to cook dishes like Somerset wild boar in cider with wild mushrooms, pancakes cooked with three local cheeses, or venison with red wine and juniper and some smoked pork sausage. Unlicensed it may be, but hospitality ensures a sherry with your hosts in the drawing room before dinner.

Westcountry dishes: wild boar in cider; apple pancakes with cider brandy; Dorset crab cakes with caper sauce.

EAST WOODLANDS

P

Horse and Groom

East Woodlands, Frome, BA11 5LY.

🍽 **12.00–14.00, 18.30–21.00 except Sun evening and all day Mon.**

☎ **01373 462802.**

🚘 **on Frome by-pass, A361 Shepton Mallet –Devizes road.**

🍽🍽 **£16.**

The pub presents a clean, white face to the world, and is nicely placed for fugitives from Longleat's lions to collapse breathless into chairs in front of the big stone hearth. Wait there, with a tankard of Cotleigh perhaps, until a table is free in the conservatory, or simply pick something from the bar menu. It's an adventurous menu: a salad of home-smoked duck breast with balsamic vinegar dressing, or Nepalese-style chicken with cardamom and cumin, and puddings such as Cumberland rum nicky, but not yet Somerset apple cake. Perhaps that will come in time.

Westcountry dishes: chicken and cider bake.

EXFORD

H

Crown Hotel

Exford, TA24 7PP.

🍽 **Restaurant 19.00–21.30.**

☎ **01643 831554; fax 01643 831665.**

🛏 **£42.**

🛏 **£84.**

🍽🍽 **£35.**

The Crown serves as a good base for sportsmen anxious to sleep close to their quarry. And walkers, too, will find the moors on their doorstep after a mega-breakfast. The bar offers lighter, cheaper alternatives to the restaurant, and does lunch as well as supper. In both, Andrew Dixon puts on a fine show to encourage shooters or fishermen to greater feats on the morrow, or remind them a little of the city they have forsaken: it is not rustic cookery. A sign of the wealth of materials now available is the cheeseboard, which may have up to 20 Westcountry cheeses. Had this been 25 years ago, they would have been lucky to find a half-dozen.

FROME
R
Crofts
21 Fromefield, Frome, BA11 2HE.
🍴 12.00–14.00 (Sun only), 19.00–21.45 (Weds–Sat).
Annual closure: 24 Dec–1 Jan.
☎ 01373 472149.
🍴🍴 £21.90.

Margaret Graham has been here six years, trying to please people with sensible prices, allied to 'quality and experimentation such as they might find in nearby Bath'. There is no ceremony, but fresh food handled with imagination and served with friendliness: a sure recipe for popularity. Menus range wide for inspiration, 'local' in clientele, not recipes, hence dishes such as pork in a pastry crust stuffed with apricots, or lamb with coconut, or chicken with lime and coriander. There are Somerset vibrations in the repeated appearance of local cheeses, not just Cheddar but the new-wave soft cheeses as well, exemplified by her haddock topped with a Somerset rarebit. This is an '80s variation on fish with a cheese sauce, and serves as reminder that not all rarebits (or 'rabbits' as they were first called) were Welsh. Versions of toasted cheese pop up all over southern and western Britain. The Victorian cookery writer and wit Dr Kitchiner complained, 'One would think nothing could be easier that to prepare a Welsh Rabbit, yet not only in private families, but at taverns, it is very seldom sent to table in perfection.' He should have asked Margaret Graham.

Westcountry dishes: **money bags with Cornish crab; apple and leek pancakes with cider sauce; haddock with Somerset rarebit topping; chocolate and clotted-cream ice-cream.**

HINTON CHARTERHOUSE

H

Homewood Park

Hinton Charterhouse, BA2 6BB.

🍴12.00–14.00, 19.00–21.30.

☎ 01225 723731; fax 01225 723820.

🍴🍴 £27 (lunch), £37 (dinner).

🛏 £95.

🛌 £98.

Homewood is one of the most comfortable country-house
hotels. It avoids overweening grandeur, yet takes us out of
the daily rut and gives grace to our hard-pressed lives: that,
surely, is part of its appeal. Another part is the cooking,
which has gained in reputation these last few years.
Gary Jones is working in the metropolitan style of
Britain's highest flyers, with dishes such as a confit of
foie gras infused with bay leaves or noisette of venison on
a gingered brioche with winter vegetables, and he is not
afraid to tackle recipes for offal that are so popular with
cooks in London,but usually less so in the country, witness
his pig's trotter with sweetbreads, black pudding and a
rosemary gravy. The quality of produce is universally
praised, although wider than the region. Mention has to
be made for Stinking Bishop, a cheese on their board
eloquent in name and flavour.

KINGSDON

P

Kingsdon Inn

Kingsdon, TA11 7LG.

🍴12.00–14.00, 19.00–22.00 (not Sun evenings).

☎ 01935 840543.

🚌 just off the B1351 Ilchester to Somerton road, N of
the A 303.

🍴🍴 £6 (lunch), £16 (dinner).

A gaily planted flagstone path leads to the front door of this thatched and picturesque inn, all beams and settles. On the cookery front, evenings are the most ambitious but praise is warm for the bar food as well as anything more elaborate. Shooters and gamekeepers must feel at home with venison, pigeon and rabbit to choose from on a single night, but there is a good range of fish (mostly from Newlyn), and substantial meats like half a roast duck with scrumpy sauce.

KILVE
P
Hood Arms

Kilve, TA5 1EA.
🍴12.00–14.00, 18.30–21.30.
☎ 01278 741210; fax 01278 741477.
🍴🍴 £15.
🛏 £38.
🛏 £44.

There are new licensees at this popular inn. The village is the last stop on a lane running down from the Quantocks before you reach the sea. Vanessa Eason writes up her offerings on a blackboard, changing as supplies come and go, and is introducing a larger slice of home-cookery to the food in dishes such as roast pork with apple sauce, Somerset apple and raspberry pie, cider and apple chicken and home-baked local ham.

LANGLEY MARSH
H
Langley House

Langley Marsh, Wiveliscombe, TA4 2UF.
🍴19.30–20.30.
Annual closure: Feb.
☎ 01984 623318; fax 01984 624573.
🖳 follow signs to Langley Marsh from Wiveliscombe.
🍴🍴 £33.
🛏 £68.50.
🛏 £90.

Peter Wilson's meals are as delicately constructed and finely judged as are the atmosphere and decoration of this elegant small country house with overflowing vegetable garden and verdant pleasure grounds. That vegetable patch may dictate the rhythm of the menus and the cookery as much as any shopping expedition, and it lends immediacy to the cookery which, almost to the last item (always excepting the inevitable exotics – coffee, chocolate, tea, etc.) have come from within the radius of Somerset and Devon. Dinners proceed with little or no choice until the final course: then, hold your horses. An elderflower and elderberry syllabub, for instance, is partnered by four or five other sweet things.

Westcountry dishes: Exmoor venison with honey and orange sauce.

LANGLEY MARSH
P
Three Horseshoes
Langley Marsh, Wiveliscombe, TA4 2UL.
12.00–14.00, 19.00–21.30.
☎ 01984 623763
£12.

John Hopkins seems to have an impressive garage. A photograph of the pub has an array of vintage sports cars that would make most customers drool even more than the thought of Marella Hopkins' home-cooking. Customers like eating here because they can watch the vegetables grow before they get put in the pot. They are keen gardeners as well as mechanics; and good at barrel-tapping, beer-lovers assert. The menus include an array of pizzas (normal or enormous in size), and some fairly usual pub dishes, but the vegetarian food is well recommended as are the game pies, rabbit casserole and other daily specials.

Westcountry dishes: Somerset fish pie; pigeon cooked in cider and cream.

LUXBOROUGH
H
Royal Oak of Luxborough
Luxborough, TA23 0SH.
🍴11.00–14.00, 18.30–22.00.
☎ 01984 640319; fax 01984 640216.
🚌 **between Roadwater and Wheddon Cross.**
🍴🍴 £15–£18.
🛏 £25.
🛏 £35.

To call this pub picturesque is a monumental understatement. Lorna Doone, where are you now? Give or take the odd curry and lasagne, the food might figure in a Doonish film: it majors on good meat, simply presented. In winter, add good game to the list. In summer, think good fish. Venison casserole with three berry sauce, and home-made pasties may keep the most energetic Exmoor rambler on their feet, and if they do not suffice, the list of puddings (supplemented from the blackboard) will fill remaining gaps. Bread and butter, steamed treacle, spotted dick are three to start. Beers in the wood.

Westcountry dishes: **pork and cider casserole.**

MIDDLECOMBE
H
Periton Park Hotel
Middlecombe, Minehead, TA24 8SW.
🍴19.00-21.00.
Annual closure: Jan.
☎ 01643 706885.
🚌 **on A39 Minehead-Porlock road.**
🍴🍴 £25.50.
🛏 £52.
🛏 £84.

Horses graze on the other side of the fence (you can ride them if you are able), gardens surround the hotel in flowery splendour, Exmoor beckons, and the dining-room offers the chance to taste Devon beef, shellfish and fish from the south coast, Exmoor venison, goat's cheese from Lubborne and local Gressingham ducks. Veal may be cooked with a Beenleigh Blue sauce; Lubborne goats' cheese is marinated in oil and herbs like a crottin de chèvre; and in the winter the orchards yield their fruit for a hot and well spiced apple tart.

Westcountry dishes: **Exmoor venison with cranberry sauce.**

NORTH CURRY
<u>P</u>

Rising Sun Inn

Knapp, North Curry, TA3 6BE.

🍴 12.00–14.00, 19.00–21.30.

☎ 01823 490436.

🍴🍴 £25.

🛏 £25.

🛏 £36.

Fish from Brixham and St Mawes, and beef from closer to home are the twin attractions at this Somerset longhouse and they keep the place bursting at the seams with people anxious to eat their fill of sole, lobster, brill or turbot, rib-eye steak or roast beef on Sundays. No-one has a bad word to say about it, or them, or about the eel smoked by Michael Brown at Bowden's Farm, Hambridge, nearby. There is bar food if something simpler is required. After lunch, go out into the district and find a withy basket: this is the place to buy them.

RUDGE
P
Full Moon

Rudge, BA11 2QF.

🍴 12.00–14.30, 19.00–21.30.

☎ 01373 830936; fax 01373 831366.

🍴🍴 £20.

🛏 £35.

🛏 £50.

The Moon is always full, because it's successful. It was Freehouse of the Year in 1994. There is bar food as well as more formal eating in the restaurant, and room enough in the additional buildings to have a sit-down wedding for nigh on a hundred guests. The cooking makes good use of local materials though menus are designed to appeal, perhaps, to a wider market.

Westcountry dishes: **pork with cider.**

SHEPTON MALLET
R
Blostin's

29 Waterloo Road, Shepton Mallet, BA4 5HH.

🍴19.00–21.30, Tues–Sat.

Annual closure: 2 weeks Jan, 2 weeks Jun.

☎ 01749 343648.

🚘 **on B3136 out of Shepton Mallet.**

🍴🍴 £22.

It is not obvious what is in Shepton Mallet's air that causes good restaurants to spring up and flourish, but it has more than the usual country-town share. Blostin's has been going for years: Nick Reed justifies his existence by offering proper cooking at sensible prices, in surroundings that might once have been called 'bistro' (there is a blackboard menu for example) – but more comfortable than that implies. No cookery out of history books, but a modern regional vernacular that makes best use of what's fresh,

be it wild boar or venison, fruit and veg. grown in nearby
Pilton, Westcountry cheeses, or wines from Pilton Manor
and Bagborough Vineyard.

Westcountry dishes: guinea fowl with apples and cider;
smoked Denhay ham with fresh figs; grilled Somerset goats'
cheese; apple and Somerset cider brandy sorbet.

SHEPTON MALLET
R (WITH ROOMS)
Bowlish House

Wells Road, Shepton Mallet, BA4 5JD.
🍽️**19.00–21.30 (and Sun lunch on first Sun of each
month).**
Annual closure: 1 week autumn, 1 week spring.
☎ **01749 342022.**
🛏️ **£48.**
🛎️ **£48.**
🍽️🍽️ **£29.15.**

Pedimented windows greet you like eyebrows at this fine
Georgian townhouse on the way out of Shepton Mallet,
a restaurant with so fine a wine list that diners will be
tempted to take a room for the ensuing night. Linda
Morley's holidays must have some time included the spice
markets of north Africa: chickpea fritter 'felafel', guinea
fowl with chili, ginger and coriander, aubergine soup with
sesame and coriander, pork with cardamom, onion and
potato soup with cumin, are are few on the list of Middle
East or orientally inspired dishes. The Westcountry might
not get a look in, but regional materials are given their due,
both by credits on the menu, and in dishes like Cheddar
cheese and chive soufflé; pheasant from Marlborough with
bacon, celeriac and apple; or a plate of good local cheeses.
The wine list includes Bagborough Special Reserve 1994
by Stephen Brooksbank as one of the excellent choice of
house wines.

Westcountry dishes: toasted Somerset goats' cheese; chicken
stuffed with fresh herbs and Denhay air-dried ham.

SHEPTON MALLET

H

Charlton House

Shepton Mallet, BA4 4PR.

🍴 12.30–14.00, 19.30–21.30.

☎ 01749 342008; fax 01749 346362.

🍴🍴 £45.

🛏 £65.

🛏 £110.

Many people will be pleased by the revival of this elegant Georgian house as a hotel. It had a fine run in the '70s, and deserved another canter. Others will be delighted at the news that Trevor Brooks, who made his name as chef and owner of Table restaurant in Babbacombe, is working again in surroundings that do him credit. His style of cooking has always been ambitious, never one to settle for the homely, and early menus underline the fact, with dishes such as salmon seared with Cajun spices, wasabi butter, spinach and Oriental rice pilaff, corn-fed chicken with gewürztraminer and crème fraîche, and truffled tagliatelle. There is an endorsement of local suppliers like Morfs Herbs in Portishead for vegetables, or Luscombe the Totnes butcher for lamb, and the wine list offers Pilton Manor and Mumford wines.

Westcountry dishes: breast of Quantock duckling with cider fondant potatoes and a spiced cider sauce; apple and cider mousse.

SHEPTON MONTAGUE

P

Montague Inn

Shepton Montague, BA9 8JW.

🍴 12.00–14.00, 19.30–21.30 (Tues–Sat).

Annual closure: first two weeks Jan.

☎ 01749 813213.

🍴🍴 £18.50.

🛏 £28.

🛏 £45.

Shepton Montague is the home of Keen's Cheddar cheese, one of the very best. Visitors will no doubt want to try it at this very stylish pub – done over and revived by David and Valerie Haskey – before buying a ton or two to age in their cellar back home. The cooking here is more than hunks of bread and cheese. Rozanne Maclean produces what might be described as 'French influenced' dishes – that's where she trained – but there are many signs of skill in marketing and sourcing of ingredients to create her own repertoire.

Westcountry dishes: **pork in farmhouse cider cream sauce; mussel soup with saffron and leeks.**

SHIPHAM
H
Daneswood House

Cuck Hill, Shipham, BS25 1RD.
⑪ **12.00–14.30, 19.00–21.00.**
☎ **01934 843145; fax 01934 843824.**
⌂ **leave A38 Bristol–Bridgewater road for Shipham, hotel is on road to Cheddar from village.**
⑪⑪ **£30.**
🛏 **from £59.50.**
🛏 **from £69.50.**

Daneswood was a homeopathic health hydro in Edwardian days. Today's version of these establishments is probably the country–house hotel. Punters don't so much need medication, but protection from the worries of everyday life and from the deadly grind of cooking and clearing-up if their lot is to care for others. So the hydro becomes hotel in one easy bound, though in the case of Daneswood, with much new building and decorating by David and Elise Hodges to fit it for its new function. The style of Julian Prosser's kitchen is more that national blend of country-housery than ethnic Somerset, but has gained plaudits even so. Expect to see Cheddar cheese given a fair outing (the Gorge is a walk away), for example in a twice-baked soufflé as a first course.

SIMONSBATH

<u>H</u>
Simonsbath House Hotel
Simonsbath, TA24 7SH.
19.00–20.00.
Annual closure: Dec–Jan.
☎ **01643 831259; fax 01643 831557.**
£25.
£54.
£92.

In spring, the house looks as if it might be drowned
beneath an advancing wave of rhododendron blossom.
However, it has been here since the seventeenth century
and is man enough to cope with any weeds. Visitors will
find it comfortable and intriguing, with a panelled library
and bar, yet another inglenook and character a-plenty. Sue
Burns offers a short dinner menu that includes English and
Exmoor overtones in dishes such as venison braised in beer
with shallots, or admirable roasts of beef or lamb, and
sweets like bread and butter pudding, or apple pie. It makes
a sustaining finish to what was probably a strenuous day out
of doors.

Westcountry dishes: rack of lamb with apple and cider
sauce.

STAPLE FITZPAINE

P

Greyhound Inn

Staple Fitzpaine, TA3 5SP.

🍴 12.00–14.00, 19.00–22.00.

☎ 01823 480227; fax 01823 480719.

🍴🍴 £20–£25.

The Greyhound is one of those pubs that barely stands still: it has an annual fun day for children, a beer festival, live music on Thursdays, a comedy turn once a month, and still has time to supply beef from their own farm for the grill. Bar food there is, but there is also a daily menu which scales greater heights. The beef connection means that meat here should be taken seriously, be it roast saddle of Somerset venison, duck breast with orange sauce, or pork with mustard.

Westcountry dishes: steak and kidney pie; scrumpy apple pie; cider pork chops.

STON EASTON

H

Ston Easton Park

Ston Easton, BA3 4QF.

🍴 12.00–14.00, 19.30–21.30.

☎ 01761 241631; fax 01761 241377.

🍴🍴 £35 (lunch), £45 (dinner).

🛏 £145.

🛏 £175.

This is a mansion. The garden is a landscape. The rooms might be in a palace. High living in great elegance, with all manner of service undertaken before the thought has even crossed your mind. Dining takes place in lighter, less obviously aristocratic surroundings, perhaps less daunting than that exquisite plaster work. The cookery is as upper-crust as it should be: light, eloquent, clever and good. A line in traditional British eating is hardly to be expected, but the materials are exemplary for things like a ragout of Cornish seafood, a warm salad of Somerset Capricorn goats' cheese with a tapénade, or a salad of pigeon breast with a gravy perfumed with lavender. This is a good place to see how a regional cuisine might develop if it were allowed an identity.

TAUNTON
H

Castle Hotel

Castle Green, Taunton, TA1 1NF.
🍽 12.30–14.00, 19.30–21.00.
☎ 01823 272671; fax 01823 336066.
🍽🍽 £32.
🛏 £80.
🛏 £120.

For many years, owner Kit Chapman has stressed his commitment to local growers and suppliers and to exploring the implications of English cookery. The way suppliers are listed and acknowledged in every menu at the Castle is proof of his intention, and a practise that others might usefully copy. At the stoves, Phil Vickery is a willing and capable partner whose inventions are both exciting and good to eat. The idea that 'English cookery' is an exercise in fuddy-duddy or artsy heritage revivalism is wonderfully scotched by such things as spring onion mashed potatoes, brill with braised chicory, capers and candied lemon, scallops with bubble and squeak and deep-fried basil, or vanilla blancmange with saffron syrup and shortbread (a winner, this). This is creative cooking that manages to draw on the experience of previous generations, then build upon the foundations to make a new and enduring superstructure. It does not rely, as does much modern British cooking, on merely importing foreign notions and interpreting them for British palates or conditions. If Westcountry Cooking has a future (as well as a past), it must turn to the likes of Phil Vickery. The Castle is a sumptuous hotel in the middle of Taunton – on the site of the original castle. From the laps of luxury that are the bedrooms, to the comfortable bars where tea may be taken of an afternoon, it runs on oiled lines.

Westcountry dishes: potted pheasant and duck with spiced pears; a selection of bilberry (whortleberry) desserts.

WEST CAMEL

P

Walnut Tree

West Camel, BA22 7QW.

📶 **12.00–14.00, 19.15–21.30.**

☎ **01935 851292.**

🍴🍴 **£12.**

🛏 **£39.50.**

🛏 **£49.50.**

The walnut tree still stands in the garden, but much of the rest of this pub has been rebuilt and refurbished in recent years. Food is the main attraction (as well as some nicely converted bedrooms) and a daily blackboard menu offers good fish up from Poole (sea bream with mushrooms, pollock with tomato and white wine), or something slightly off the beaten culinary track, such as wild boar sausages.

WEST HATCH

R

Nightingales

Bath House Farm, West Hatch, TA3 5RH.

📶 **12.30–15.00 (Sun lunch), 19.30–21.30 (Fri,Sat dinner); other times by arrangement.**

Annual closure: 1 week Oct, 2 weeks Feb.

☎ **01823 480806.**

🍴🍴 **£27.**

The tidal wave of Italian recipes and Italian style swept over Nightingales leaving many dishes and ideas in its wake: rabbit with pancetta, tarragon, wild mushroom risotto and a mustard sauce; roast tomatoes with focaccia; prawns and scallops with linguine; roast onions with melted fontina and basil oil, are some of them. In some ways, it typifies the character of British cooking, always happy to plunder abroad for inspiration. Equally, this is how many nations have grafted new concepts on to grandmother's cooking. Even the Italians knew nothing of tomatoes until they were brought back from America. So one should not cavil at good cookery, whatever its character, especially if, as in the case of Nightingales, they materials are sourced freshly and directly. New ideas give new angles, as in their apple and raspberry crumble made with cornmeal (another New World introduction to the Italians). It all makes the world go round.

Westcountry dishes: cornmeal, apple and raspberry crumble cake.

WILLITON
<u>H</u>
White House
Williton, TA4 4QW.
🍽 **19.30–21.00.**
Annual closure: early Nov–May.
☎ **01984 632777, 632306.**
🍽🍽 **£36.**
🛏 **£32.**
🛏 **£56.**

'Fanatically fresh,' writes Dick Smith of his food and cooking at this comfortable village hotel where he has been welcoming guests for the past thirty years. Lately, there has been a shift of emphasis from meat to fish cookery, for the best of reasons: Dick's fish supplies have come up to the standard he would like. The importance of origin and seasonality shines through the menus, which barely reflect the ebb and flow of fashion, but much more what was in the basket this morning. Duck, for example, is cooked with mulberry sauce (the fruit bought from Pixford Fruit Farm in Bishop's Lydeard), or pigeon is served with beetroot and a multiplicity of salad leaves. Cheeses are invariably from the Westcountry.

Westcountry dishes: Devon squab pie.

Wiltshire

Introduction

The expanse of Salisbury Plain divides north from south and the county seems to look four ways towards other regions than the South West. It moves imperceptibly into Hampshire on one side, merges gracefully with Oxfordshire on another, is part of the increasing home-counties continuum towards Berkshire, and remains firmly attached to the South West only where it touches Somerset and Gloucestershire. The Plain is the hub, the central mountain away from which all else slides.

Say Wiltshire, think pig. This would be the automatic reaction of anyone old enough to have travelled west from London on the old Bath road. The giant factories of Calne, source of bacon and pork pies, impressed their image on the memory. Downsized now, or gone, but pig and pork left its mark on Wiltshire cookery, or at least its traditions. Fortunate, therefore, that Sandridge Farm at Bromham still produces bacon fit to eat – served in many guest house dining-rooms. Bradenham ham, although not named after a Wiltshire village, became a Wiltshire recipe, immediately identifiable by its blackened rind, the product of a sweet, treacly, juniper and spice pickle.

Wiltshire cheese is also but a memory, although one revived by Jo Hale at Blaydon Hill Farm. Henrietta Green, in her description of this in *Food Lovers' Guide to Britain*, retells the story of the proverb 'as different as chalk and cheese'. It referred indeed to Wiltshire and the divide between the sheep-supporting chalk uplands (where everyone was Church of England) and the cattle-grazing valleys (where they were Chapel). In Jane Austen's *Emma*, the end of a meal is described consisting of Stilton and North Wiltshire cheeses, butter, celery, beetroot, and dessert.

Warminster was famed for its corn market, Marlborough for cattle, Calne for pigs, and the uncultivated forests (Savernake and Cranborne Chase) ran thick with game. The county was well blessed. The rich water meadows of the valleys supported well fattened stock, and the rivers and chalk streams yielded crayfish and freshwater fish, even if the county itself was landlocked.

Large swathes of the county are today occupied by incomers, who can reach London or Bristol in minutes rather than hours, or by the military, who have brought Salisbury Plain into national service, or by city-born denizens of the new megalopolis – creatures of the east-west motorway that has revived the fortunes of Swindon. Opening up the boundaries like this has caused cooks to look beyond for inspiration, and signs of locality are none too plentiful.

Some local dishes:

Bradenham ham
Bradenham chaps
Brawn
Pork pie
Devizes veal pie
Lardy cake
Wiltshire porkies of sausagemeat, batter and apple
Ham and egg toasts

ALVEDISTON
P (WITH ROOMS)
Crown Inn

Alvediston, SP5 5JY.

🍴 12.00–15.00, 19.00–22.30.

☎ 01722 780335.

🚗 3 m S of A30 Salisbury to Shaftesbury road, turn off at Ansty.

🛏 £20.

🛏 £45.

🍴🍴 £21.50.

Once we are globally warmed, kangaroo will be a local ingredient. As it is, it stays a sign of this hyper-country pub's adventurous bar and dining-room food. There are many other reasons to visit: fish from Poole, local game, venison pie, wild-boar ragout, Dorset lamb and an attractive garden for summer meals *al fresco*.

AVEBURY
R
Stones

High Street, Avebury, SN8 1RF.

🍴 10.00–18.00 (every day Easter–Oct, and some weekends Nov–Mar).

Annual closure: Nov–Jan.

☎ 01672 539514; fax 01672 539683.

🍴🍴 £16.

From nowhere, Stones has come to represent much that is enterprising in British vegetarian cookery, and the green movement generally. Michael Pitts and Hilary Howard comment that they have three acres of land in Avebury where they grow as much of their own produce as possible (and recycle the waste from the kitchen into tons of compost). The very ethos of the place means that much is made of local purchasing and local producers. Of course, vegetarian cookery is relatively new in Britain and has recently plundered ideas and flavours from the world at large making it more enjoyable than in the days of nut cutlets all round. The Westcountry has recipes that could slot into this tradition (Devonshire stew is all vegetable), because the people were too poor to eat meat every day. However, they were not vegetarian because they liked vegetables. If they had the opportunity, they would usually make a dish more savoury with a small addition of meat. The Cornish likky (leek) pie served at Stones is vegetarian, but in the original, leeks and bacon are layered in a pastry case and at the end of cooking, the juices are poured out and replaced with clotted cream and eggs to make a rich custard binding.

Westcountry dishes: Cornish likky pie (using clotted cream and cider).

BRADFORD ON AVON
<u>H</u>
Woolley Grange
Woolley Green, Bradford on Avon, BA15 1TX.
🍴 **12.30–14.00, 19.30–22.00.**
☎ **01225 864705; fax 01225 864059.**
🍴🍴 £35.
🛏 £90.
🛏 £96.

The Chapmans have made their name for the most child-friendly fancy country-house hotel in these islands. It's a brilliant ploy – some people have children – but does not detract either from the comfort and beauty of house and garden, or from the quality of the cooking. Lunchtime is more relaxed and free-form than dinner, but the main-stream modern British style is evident at both meals, in dishes like chargrilled tuna with polenta and salsa verde. Local ingredients have their place, and some interesting interpretations do surface: crisp roast belly of Gloucester Old Spot pork with creamed potatoes and onion and gherkin sauce, or chicken with sage and onion stuffing and pancetta (Italian salted belly pork) and a sage sauce.

BURTON
P
Old House at Home
Burton, SN14 7LT.
⏰ **12.00–14.00 (except Tues), 19.00–22.00 (21.30 Sun).**
☎ **01454 218227.**
🚗 **on the B4039 Chipping Sodbury to Chippenham road.**
🍴🍴 **£14.50.**

The Warburtons won the accolade of Pub Caterers of the Year in 1997. Their pub has grown and grown since they took it over thirteen long years ago, and offers a bewildering range of food in bar and restaurant, including special themed nights every so often. Despite its name, the cookery is more international than home, for instance with lots of rice dishes and ideas redolent of big-city eateries. Those in search of local foods may be best pleased with the fish: a good range, skilfully cooked. There is no doubt at all, however, that it draws the crowds.

COLERNE
H
Lucknam Park
Colerne, SN14 8AZ.
🍴 **12.30–14.30, 19.30–21.30.**
☎ **01225 742777; fax 01225 743536.**
🚗 **signed from the crossroads for Colerne village on the road between Ford (on the A420) and Batheaston (on the A4).**
🍴🍴 **£30 (lunch), £50 (dinner).**
🛏 **£130.**
🛏 **£160.**

A grand country-house hotel, complete with a mile-long tree-lined drive and a health spa. The public rooms are both handsome and deeply relaxing, the service amiable and constant. Cooking at such a place draws its driving force from fashion and practice in circles far removed from its immediate region, yet it is a fact that often kitchens at this level of endeavour will put a gloss on local materials few residents will have thought of. Lucknam has always prided itself on its fish cookery, and the tradition lives on, with deliveries from Cornwall contributing to dishes such as salmon, scallops and lobster in a ginger and saffron sauce, or brill with jerusalem artichokes and thyme, or their delicious crab bisque with a ginger and lime glaze. Lighter meals are also available at lunchtime, making this a great excursion from a hard day in Bath. The wine list includes four wines from Mumford's Vineyard at Bannerdown near Bath.

EBBESBOURNE WAKE
P

Horseshoe Inn

Ebbesbourne Wake, SP5 5JF.

🍽 **12.00–14.00, 19.00–21.30 (Tues–Sat, Sun & Mon lunch).**

☎ **01722 780474.**

🚪 **between Salisbury and Shaftesbury, just off the A30..**

🍽🍽 **£15.**

🛏 **£25.**

🛏 **£40.**

Anthony and Patricia Bath have been looking after locals and visitors alike for more years than they care to mention. There is a timelessness to the pub, and a charm to the situation – aided and abetted by goats and a pot-bellied pig that do not contribute to the menu. Cooking is home-cooking, fresh and wholesome, though Westcountry in resources rather than style. However, look for Patricia Bath's butcher's faggots on the bar menu, or duckling with gooseberry sauce, steak and kidney pie, or venison pie, or eat in the small restaurant apart from the bar. Good cider available.

FORD

H

White Hart

Ford, SN14 8RP.

12.00–14.30, 19.00–22.00.

☎ **01249 782213; fax 01249 783075.**

£12.50 (lunch), £21.50 (dinner).

£45.

£65.

'Established 1553, the old inn by the trout stream,' runs
the inscription, although the style and welcome is of this
century, not that. Imagine if Queen Elizabeth I were served
banoffi pie. The food here is good, and it is popular. When I
visit the industrial estate in Chippenham close by, this is the
place they always send me for lunch. There are extensive
menus, for bar and dining-room, and one thing that may be
worth exploring is their pork – it is Wiltshire, after all.

Westcountry dishes: terrine of ham hock and pork knuckle
with button onions and a pea purée; wild boar sausages with
celeriac, baked apple and grain mustard; loin of pork with
caramelized apples and sweet cider sauce.

GRITTLETON

<u>B&B</u>

Church House

Grittleton, SN14 6AP.

🍴20.00.

☎ 01249 782562; fax 01249 782546.

🍴🍴 £16.50.

🛏 £30.

🛏🍴 £54.50.

Looking at this house, the twentieth-century traveller may wish he had been an eighteenth-century clergyman: no stinting here, from the columned front door, to the gracious staircase, the attached wings, and the eleven acres of gardens that stretch beyond. Life at Church House still reflects some of those bygone rhythms, even though the stables contain a swimming pool, not carriages. Dinner is taken by all the guests together, at a single large table, with a stately succession of courses, described as 'British eclectic' by the owner Anna Moore, but often drawing on the Church House garden for herbs, vegetables and soft fruits, and neighbours and local growers for the meat, dairy and heavy protein sections of the meal. Church House is a reminder that travellers these days are well served by the category described as 'Bed & Breakfast'. No longer is it damp sheets and asking the landlady's permission for a bath, but provides accommodation either more luxurious or more enticing and exhilarating than many a fancy hotel.

HINDON

<u>P</u>

Lamb at Hindon

Hindon, SP3 6DP.

🍴12.00–14.00, 19.00–21.30.

☎ 01747 820573; fax 01747 820605.

🚗 1 mile S of the A303 on the B3089.

🍴🍴 £23.

🛏 £38.

🛏🍴 £55.

This substantial country inn has a long history: a
seventeenth-century fabric, medieval origins, a close
connection with the life of Hindon town through all the
centuries, yet kept smart and livable until the present day.
By the beginning of this century, when Hindon was less
than dynamic, the great nature and travel writer W.H.
Hudson stayed here to polish off his book A Shepherd's
Life and wrote, 'so rustic and pretty amidst the green
swelling downs with great woods crowning the heights
beyond.' It is possible to meet a fillet of kangaroo on the
way from kitchen to dining-room (there is also an excellent
bar menu), but Westcountry fans will probably wish to
concentrate on game like venison, pigeon, wild duck or
pheasant (or a mixture in the game casserole), or be willing
to settle for fish from the South West.

Westcountry dishes: medallions of Fonthill venison with
juniper berry sauce.

LACOCK
R (WITH ROOMS)
At the Sign of the Angel
6 Church Street, Lacock, SN15 2LA.
🍽 **12.30–14.00, 19.30–21.00, except Mon lunch.**
Annual closure: 23–31 Dec.
☎ **01249 730230; fax 01249 730527.**
🍽🍽 **£20.**
🛏 **£55.**
🛏 **£80.**

Visitors battle through thickets of film crews shouting,
'Lights–Camera–Action,' so picturesque and perfect is the
setting. The Sign of the Angel swings merrily in the midst,
tourists happy with the ambience of heritage, while the
hungry settle down to contemplate Wiltshire pigs and their
produce. Honey-roasted ham hock is pleasingly alliterative,
and there is plenty of bacon from Sandridge Farm at
Bromham. The lovers of wildlife will go for the wild-boar
sausages. Wood panelling, stunted doorcases, and ancient
flagstones contribute to the atmosphere, and the food is in

similar key, avoiding the prettified with substantial contributions like Mrs Levis's steak and kidney pudding or a pigeon terrine with damson sauce. Meringues with clotted cream get votes of confidence and the cheeseboard is all-English. In the garden they grow their own asparagus, lots of produce, and keep their own chickens, while on days-off they rush out to catch some fish for the next menu. Good breakfasts. Try the Mumfords wine from Bannerdown.

Westcountry dishes: Wiltshire ham hock with honey mustard sauce.

MARLBOROUGH
<u>C</u>
Polly Tea Rooms
26-7 High Street, Marlborough, SN8 1LW.
(🍴) **all day, lunch 12.00-15.00.**
Annual closure: Christmas Day, Boxing Day.
☎ **01672 512146; fax 01672 511156.**
(🍴)(🍴) **lunch from £10 (unlicensed).**

Generations of parents delivering their children, or visiting the prisoners, in Marlborough College have breathed sighs of relief that the Polly Tea Rooms is there for refreshment, or shelter on a windy, rain-driven day. As years have passed, the Tea Rooms have moved with the culinary times: no longer cottage pie, but hello potato and cheese gnocchi with a tomato and herb sauce and spinach. Breakfast may be the best time to catch a scent of horrid schooldays: sausages and good bacon; toast and lashings of tea. Change is good for institutions, and Polly has kept her feathers smart and colourful by never resting on her laurels.

MELKSHAM
<u>R (WITH ROOMS)</u>
Toxique
187 Woodrow Road, Melksham, SN12 7AY.
(🍴) **12.30–14.30, 19.30–21.30 (Wed–Sun).**
☎ **01225 702129.**

🚗 take Calne road from centre of Melksham; after 600 yards turn left into Forest Road, Toxique on left after 1 mile.

🍴🍴 £35.

🛏 £70.

🛎 £95.

It takes a brave man with a sense of humour to call his restaurant 'poisonous'. This handsome farmhouse on the edge of Melksham is anything but that, though the characterful rooms inside show off the humour to a T. The modern tilt to the cookery is of a piece with the glowing colours and ingenuity of the decoration. Somehow, a Cornish pasty, Devizes pie, Bradenham chap or lardy cake doesn't seem to fit. This does not affect the buying policy, which is as local as can be, with venison and wild boar for those who like game, fish supplied through Bath market, and a good choice of cheese, much of it Westcountry. Duck with ginger-glazed beetroot, smoked aubergines, green beans and potato rösti, or red mullet with almond couscous, chargrilled pumpkin and Moroccan harissa may well be the shape of Westcountry cooking to come. Their apple bread and butter pudding would be an immediate candidate for adoption. Toxique have spread their wings to Bath, and have Toxique Fish at 14 North Parade (01225 445983) where the happy fusion of appeal to the eye and palate is repeated.

MERE
H
Chetcombe House Hotel
Chetcombe Road, Mere, BA12 6AZ.

🍴19.00.

☎ 01747 860219; fax 01747 860111.

🚗 from E leave A303 to Mere, hotel is on L; from W, go through Mere and Chetcombe Road is on R as you leave the town.

🍴🍴 £17.50.

🛏 £29.

🛎 £50.

Mere was always a coaching town, there is a fine old inn to prove it. Nowadays, it is a useful halfway-house to the Westcountry and the Rosses' small hotel, with plenty of garden to act as buffer to the traffic, is a well-reported refuge brimful with hospitality. A nightly menu sensibly avoids too many choices – that would only detract from freshness – but perfectly reflects the passing seasons. Too often do cooks turn to the freezer for respite from winter's chill, to give a glimmer of colour to the cold grey skies. And if it's not the freezer, then it's off to the supermarket for some delicacy from Guatemala or Central Africa. This may add to life's variety, and international profits, but goes against the grain of cooking to the rhythm of the land and the region. In August, Sue Ross followed fresh tomato soup with basil, with roast duckling with new potatoes, mange tout peas and French beans. As dessert she offered nectarines in raspberry purée. Come November, her choice ran from pear, Stilton and walnut tart, to baked gammon with mustard sauce, roast root vegetables and Savoy cabbage, to a plum nut crumble. Perfect seasonality and, needless to say, much drawn from local growers and suppliers.

MIDDLE WINTERSLOW
B&B
Beadles
Middleton, Middle Winterslow, SP5 1QS.
🍴 **12.00–14.00, 19.00–21.00.**
☎ **01980 862922.**
🍴🍴 **£15.50 (unlicensed).**
🛏 **£25.**
🛏 🛏 **£50.**

Beadles is opposite the village shop. Anne-Marie Yuille Baddeley doubtless always has this as last resort should her cupboard run bare – but it seems a rare event. A daily meal of impeccable freshness is her forte, watercress soup her speciality. Her insistence on freshness, and immediacy, is what the Westcountry Cooking initiative is all about, be it pork stuffed with prunes and pistachios, lamb with lemon, garlic and mint sauce or huss (not a fish seen often on menus nowadays) with black butter. The guest house has no licence, but the Yuille Baddeleys are happy for guests to bring their own tipple, and a glass of wine is served gratis to all diners to make the party swing.

Westcountry dishes: fresh huss in black butter.

NETTLETON
B&B
Fosse Farmhouse
Nettleton Shrub, Nettleton, SN14 7NJ.
🍴 **12.30–14.00, 19.00–21.00.**
☎ **01249 782286; fax 01249 783066.**
🚗 **from M4, take B4039 to village of The Gib, 1st left, then 1 mile on right.**
🍴🍴**£27.50.**
🛏 **£48.**
🛏 **£75.**

There is a teashop here, as well as antique shop, accommodation and restaurant. And Caron Cooper has a full life doing TV for home and abroad and cookbooks for Japan. She might stand as England personified. The antiques business supplies some of the furnishings (buy your dining table) and informs the happenstance character of the country decor. The farmhouse accommodation spreads as far as the stables, and old hay racks and cobbled floors are the decorative accompaniment to breakfast, and cream tea. Caron's suppliers are topnotch, and she is free in her acknowledgement: Wiltshire Tracklements' mustards and sauces; Hobbs House breads and baked goods; Sandridge Farm bacon and pork; Colham Mill organic meats; Rodda's clotted cream. The style of cooking is a good advertisement for the raw materials: not too tricksy, but letting them speak out their qualities.

Westcountry dishes: roast oyster bacon with honey, mustard and apple sauce; apple and cider cake; cream teas.

PITTON
P
Silver Plough
White Hill, Pitton, SP5 1DZ.
🍽12.00–14.30, 19.00–22.00.
☎ 01722 712266.
🚌 sign-posted off the A30 Salisbury–Andover road, 5 miles W of Salisbury.
🍽🍽 £20.

The produce of the local smokehouse, Fjordling's at Dunstable Farm, can be sampled in this popular restaurant-cum-pub where a printed menu is supplemented by daily specials that generally, although not exclusively, draw on ideas and styles from beyond the region in dishes like aubergine filled with ratatouille or chargrilled tuna with chilli salsa. But there is also a sound traditional pub side, with excellent ploughman's. Materials such as tuna are a poser for advocates of Westcountry Cooking. The fish are often of local origin, but the fishery is a recent phenomenon. Squid and monkfish are two other sorts that spring to mind. These were simply not caught in any great number, and not eaten, in previous centuries. So a 'heritage' style, which some might see as the intention of Westcountry Cooking, is not relevant. Ideas need to be drawn and developed from countries that have made a habit of eating these species. This does not make restaurants which serve them in this fashion the less local.

Westcountry dishes: **Dorset apple cake.**

REDLYNCH
R (WITH ROOMS)
Langley Wood

Hamptworth Road, Redlynch, SP5 2PB.

🍴12.30–14.00, (Weds–Fri & Sun), 19.30–22.30 (Weds–Sat).

☎ 01794 390348.

🚪 between Landford and Redlynch.

🍴🍴 £18.

🛏 £17.50.

🛎 £35.

The Rosens said themselves that they 'dropped out'. I only mention this because the phrase sets the right tone of relaxed, unstuffy hospitality that is this under-stated venture. All supplies are, as far as possible, local. 'We are fortunate in being able to telephone farms in the morning and collect from them produce freshly picked to order.' The woodlands around the house yield their harvest of mushrooms. The cooking which results is neither traditional, nor heavy with exotic influence: it steers a British compromise between some of the flavours and fireworks of the Mediterranean and mellower tastes of English coasts and countryside.

Westcountry dishes: Somerset cheese soup; Somerset syllabub; Westcountry rabbit; roast duck with gingered apple sauce; potted Somerset Stilton; pears with Somerset Stilton.

ROWDE
P
George and Dragon

High Street, Rowde, SN10 2PN.

🍴12.00–14.00, 19.00–22.00 (Tues–Sat).

Annual closure: 2 weeks Christmas and New Year.

☎ 01380 723053; fax 01380 724738.

🍴🍴 £25.

Not so many years ago, it seemed that all pub food would be microwaved variations of lasagne and bangers and mash and that most pubs would be lost opportunities. That was before couples like Helen and Tim Withers arrived on the scene. Today, the possibilities seem boundless for combining good, fresh food, and the serving of drink and refreshment within the confines of the British pub. Gone the days, when first I stole through saloon bar doors, when the only thing to eat was a packet of peanuts. The George and Dragon is one of the best of the new wave. The cooking is exceptional, as with-it as any big-city operation with lots of influences from the Mediterranean and Italy, yet based on a local roster of suppliers that ensure immediacy of flavour. Fish, brought straight up from Newlyn twice a week, is a big feature, usually chosen off the daily blackboard, but the menu also has items like a mushroom risotto to die for, excellent beef from Walter Rose in Devizes, simple but good vegetables like, one day, pink fir-apple potatoes and stir-fried greens from the village, and puddings that may, if lucky, include brown sugar meringues with Jersey cream or a steamed marmalade pudding. The wine list gets better by leaps and bounds and the fact it's a restaurant doesn't stop it being a pub, and having that particular daily bustle that makes pub life more fun for the casual visitor than all those starched tablecloths and bowing servitors.

TEFFONT EVIAS
H
Howards House

Teffont Evias, SP3 5RJ.
12.30–14.00 (Sun), 19.30–21.30.
☎ 01722 716392/716821; fax 01722 716380.
at Teffont, turn right at Black Horse pub.
£32.
£65.
£95.

The particular roof-line and outward appearance of this house, originally seventeenth-century but extended and remodelled in the nineteenth, and surrounded by an enviable garden, is explained by Paul Firmin as the consequence of the builder's youthful Grand Tour where he was tremendously impressed by all things Swiss. Inside, there is a pleasing spareness to the decoration: a restraint that suits the building. Paul Firmin's cookery is an intriguing amalgam of old and new: a menu might contain foie gras, ox tongue and truffle pie with a Cumberland sauce, next to chicken and goats' cheese timbale with black olives and a basil and beetroot ravioli. Mediterranean influences abound, but there are signs of locality as well: excellent game (venison, partridge, pigeon, rabbit, hare and pheasant) supplied from Hindon, and fish up from Brixham. Paul Firmin does a lot of fish dishes, even though some miles from water, and is not so snobbish as not to work with commoner species, as in his rock salmon with a shrimp bisque and saffron risotto. Cheeses are British.

WARMINSTER
H

Bishopstrow House

Warminster, BA12 9HH.

🍴12.00–14.00, 19.30–21.00.

☎ 01985 212312; fax 01985 216769.

🚪 on the B3414, 1 mile E of Warminster.

🍴🍴 £29.50 (lunch), £40 (dinner).

🛏 £75.

🛎 £110.

The house is glossy magazine made real. A colonnade juts into the swimming pool; whirlpool baths have gathered silk ceilings; there's a temple in the garden (27 acres); enough fabric goes into the curtains to stock a haberdasher's – and upholster a country cinema with the leftovers. Chris Suter's cooking is all of a piece, but comes in many levels of elaboration and expense (the cheapest being at lunchtime in the conservatory). There is an estimable tendency to explore the possibilities of English materials and cookery, so we are not just left with a sophisticated culinary tour of the world when embarking on the menu. Dishes such as fish cakes with spinach and parsley sauce, cod wrapped in

Dorset ham with a truffle oil mash, pork with local wild mushrooms in a risotto, or black pudding with apples are really worth trying. Game and rare breeds also get their share of attention: Tamworth pork is not often seen. It is exciting to see chefs of this calibre making a special effort both with local suppliers and with the idea of British cookery.

Westcountry dishes: venison saddle with baked apple and blackberry sauce; roast belly of Tamworth pork and split pea mash; braised ham hock; apple crumble and custard.

WOOTTON RIVERS
P

Royal Oak

Wootton Rivers, SN8 4NQ.

🍴12.00–14.00, 19.00–21.30.

☎ 01672 810322; fax 01672 811267.

🚌 off the A346 between Marlborough and Burbage.

🍴🍴 £13.

🛏 £20.

🍽 £30.

The name of the village may lead the unsuspecting to think 'river', but in fact it's a canal, the Kennet & Avon, and it's not far from the door. Longboat weekenders add to the crowds that throng, not least for the food. The constant bar menus run along well-grooved pub lines, good and generous for all that, but more interesting dishes will be found on the specials menu which changes frequently. Look for Wiltshire sausages with mash and onion gravy, or ham in a number of guises. Game is given fair outing in winter months, and fish supplied from Cornwall is not to be sneezed at. The wine list contains some treasures.

Westcountry dishes: Cornish crab and lobster soup; baked Wiltshire ham in Devon cider.

INDEX
GENERAL INDEX TO
PLACENAMES IN THE GUIDE

INDEX
BY NAME OF ESTABLISHMENT

INDEX
BY TYPE OF ESTABLISHMENT

Pub

Restaurant

Restaurant (with rooms)

MAIN INDEX
ARRANGED BY COUNTY

Use this index in conjunction with the
fold-out map at the back of the book.
The numbers preceding each entry in the
index identifies the approximate location
of the establishment within each county.

Cornwall

Devon

Wiltshire

THE "WESTCOUNTRY COOKING" CAMPAIGN

How can <u>you</u> support our campaign? We intend to make the Westcountry region as famous for its food, as it is for the beauty of its landscape. To have a real impact we need the whole-hearted support of the eating and drinking public. It must be, first and foremost, a consumer movement.

That is why we have launched the *Westcountry Cooking Supporters' Club*. Its members will be actively involved in the campaign, by providing reports both on existing outlets and potential new ones. Members will qualify for discounts on Westcountry Cooking publications and products and receive invitations to *Supporters' Club Events*. A regular Newsletter will include updates on who is doing what and where; special features on Guide outlets; news of new products and where to find unusual ingredients such as elvers or mazzards! Members' contributions will be particularly welcome.

Annual membership costs just £20.00 (inc VAT). You can join by completing the details below and play your part in the South West's culinary renaissance.

I would like to join the *Westcountry Cooking Supporters' Club* and enclose my cheque for £20.00 payable to Westcountry Cooking.

PLEASE PRINT

Name:..

Address:...

....

....

Daytime tel. no:..

Signature:........................... Date:...................

Please send to: Polly Addelsee, Westcountry Cooking, Taste of the West Ltd., Agriculture House, Pynes Hill, Rydon Lane, Exeter EX2 5ST

READERS COMMENTS

Westcountry Cooking is an initiative of Taste of the West Ltd and *The Guide to Good Food* is intended to be the region's premier annual food guide, with the emphasis on local produce.

We hope you have found this guide useful, practical and entertaining. We would appreciate your comments on any of the entries and on suggestions for inclusion in future editions. Please complete the form below, or write on a separate piece of paper, including your name and address, and post it to: Polly Addelsee, Westcountry Cooking, Taste of the West Ltd, Agriculture House, Pynes Hill, Rydon Lane, Exeter EX2 5ST.

Name and address of establishment:

....

....

Comments:

Your name and address:

....

....